Climate Cult

Climate Cult

A Biblical & scientific
response to climate change

John Berry

ISBN 978-0-9966012-2-1
e-book ISBN 978-0-9966012-3-8

Published in the United States of America by Big Sky

Books are available in quantity for promotional or premium use. For information on discounts and terms visit our website: www.johnberryministries.com

First edition, first publishing October 2020

"They know the truth about God because He has made it obvious to them. Forever since the world was created, people have seen the earth and sky. Through everything God made, they can clearly see his invisible qualities—his eternal power and divine nature. So they have no excuse for not knowing God."

Romans, 1:19-20 NLT

"Take no part in the worthless deeds of evil and darkness; instead, expose them"

Ephesians 5:11 NLT

CONTENTS

Foreword

I grew up as an atheist believing many of the same things that radical environmentalists do today. So I understand how easy it is to be deceived by environment issues like climate change.

I always had a love for nature and have traveled to many incredible wild places around the world. During my teenage years and young adult life I was involved with numerous environmental and conservation efforts in South Africa. Some of my greatest memories are from diving with whale sharks, stomping through swamps in search of venomous snakes, and walking through undergrowth conducting wild rhino censuses. And in the course of my career as a professional herpetologist[1] I worked on endangered reptile breeding programs and assisted National Geographic and wildlife film crews, both in the lab and in the wild. Today as a scuba diver and active kayaker, I love being out in nature. So I really understand the strong attraction many have for wildlife and the environment.

---

[1] A reptile biologist

However, once I became a born-again follower of Jesus I understood that in God's eyes, people who are eternal spirits are of far greater value than the earth and our environment, which are only temporal.

Yet even in its current fallen state[2], nature is incredible. There is nothing as beautiful as a magnificent sunset, or watching waves crashing ashore on a deserted beach at dawn. And there are few things as mesmerizing as seeing wild animals roaming free in their natural environment. So unlike many modern Christians, I reject the idea that there is no value in conservation because we are living in the last days. We have been in the last days since Jesus ascended back to heaven after rising from the grave. Yes we are closer to the Lord's return than ever before and of course our focus should be on saving people first. However, that is no excuse to ignore sensible conservation not only for our benefit but also for our children if the Lord doesn't return before we pass. Nature is good for our souls and for that reason alone conservation is very important, as long as it's in the right context.

Together with a belief in conservation, I also believe there are real environmental issues we should address. I point a few of these out at the end of the book. I don't however believe climate change is one of them, as I will explain.

My reasons for writing Climate Cult

---

[2] Due to Adam's original sin, all of creation was cursed. Genesis 3: 17 *"Since you listened to your wife and ate from the tree whose fruit I commanded you not to eat, <u>the ground is cursed because of you</u>. All your life you will struggle to scratch a living from it."*

My main reason for writing this book is to expose the common misbeliefs and deception behind the cultish theory of climate change. Cults trap people with lies and irrational obsessions. The climate cult is no different.

At least since the time of Noah, our earth has experienced numerous alternating cycles of warming and cooling weather[3]. Some have lasted for centuries others have been much shorter. While really accurate weather observations have only been possible in the last 100 years or so, history itself fills in a lot of the blanks. Many climate alarmists ignore this, basing their assumptions purely on the last century, while at the same time manipulating climate data to match their ideological agenda. And this is not just my opinion. Numerous scientists and environmentalists as we will see, are unnerved at the apocalyptic climate alarmist predictions thrown out by radical climate activists.

Many in the church too have been taken in by the irrationality of radical environmentalism. The focus of the church should always be on saving people, never on saving the planet. We are simply passing through, this is not our permanent home. The Bible tells us how the world will end and it won't be due to climate change! It will be when Jesus returns and not before. Good science, sound reasoning and ethical economics, combined with the morals of a Biblical worldview, should be the guiding principles we as believers adhere to.

So as we approach the end of this current age, many great deceptions abound as people follow their own way and ignore their Creator. My aim is to help believers have Biblical and

---

[3] We can only assume that before the global flood earth's temperature was more stable.

scientifically accurate answers to the most widely repeated junk science climate claims.

Finally, while I know many will agree with my views, I understand and accept that some will not concur with what I have written. Hopefully you will read the entire book before making any conclusions.

Who this book will benefit

This book will give intelligent answers on how to discuss climate change with family, neighbors and friends, who believe we are facing a climate emergency.

In particular, I believe every parent with school age children and teenagers should read this book. Even if only in part, to better understand the secular intellectual reprogramming that is occurring in our education system. It will give you an insight into what your children are being taught to believe at school.

Lastly those in ministry; pastors; youth pastors; young adult pastors; middle school and high school pastors, will find useful answers to help those they work with. Even while coronavirus has taken a lot of the limelight recently, climate change is still a top of mind issue with many people. There are literally millions of articles, press releases, blogs and social media posts every year discussing and promoting the topic. To give you an idea of how sizable the online tsunami of climate change data is, searching for the term "climate change" on Google returns over 1.1 billion results[1]. That's way more than results for the "Dallas Cowboys"(188 million), the "New York Yankees"(118 million) and "Justin Bieber"(330 million) combined!

Introduction

From the beginning God planned and created all of creation with a two fold purpose. Firstly the universe, including our earth and all living creatures and plants reveal God Himself as the Creator. Jesus regularly used examples from nature when He taught. And secondly, the earth was created as the perfect home where mankind could live and thieve.

"The heavens proclaim the glory of God. The skies display His craftsmanship. Day after day they continue to speak; night after night they make Him known. They speak without a sound or word; their voice is never heard. Yet their message has gone throughout the earth, and their words to the entire world."
Psalms 19:1-4 NLT

Yet in modern secular Western culture, instead of giving glory to the Creator for His creation, nature has been hijacked and our planet personified. People talk about "Mother Earth" needing to be preserved. We witness environmentalists engaging in systematic exaggerations of science in order to promote their secular ideological agenda. They think they are working for some greater good, and they justify blowing perceived environmental threats out of all proportion. Furthermore rather than viewing the earth as a home for mankind, humans are seen as a harmful invasive species, whose numbers need to be controlled, in order to preserve planet earth.

Today we even have progressive seminaries and churches "confessing their climate sins to plants" and calling for their congregations to support environmental causes. They literally treat the environment as sacred. This is wrong. They don't realize the deception they are involved with.

God created this planet as our home and gave us incredible animals and an environment to enjoy. And He created natural resources for us to use. He never intended for mankind to worship His creation but to rather use and steward it wisely.

Even so as we begin our journey to expose and debunk the climate change agenda, I will present 4 key truths that will help our understanding.

4 Key truths about climate change

<u>Truth #1:</u> The climate change agenda is strongly antihuman

"Instead of controlling the environment for the benefit of the population, perhaps we should control the population to ensure the survival of our environment"

Sir David Attenborough, naturalist and prolific wildlife documentary narrator

The modern environmentalism movement sees human beings as the biggest obstacle to saving the planet. You and I are blamed for all kinds environmental problems. Secular environmentalists frequently refer to people as "a virus", "parasites", "a disease" and "the worst thing that ever happened to the planet". This worldview is in total contrast to what God says. He sees mankind as being more important than all of creation.

The antihuman attitude has been gaining ground for years. Today there are more and louder calls to reduce the global human population than ever before, especially coming from the United Nations and other secular government leaders.

This same secular mindset can be seen in many of the policies and proposals used by the promoters of climate change when they suggest "depopulation". By this they mean two things (1) sterilizing and stopping people from having children and (2) killing more people in the name of saving the planet.

- Chapter 4: The antihuman agenda, covers this in more detail

Truth #2: Climate alarmists deliberately target and use children

"A genocide like the Holocaust is happening again, on a far greater scale, and in plain sight, from climate change."

Roger Hallam, co-founder of activist group Extinction Rebellion in an interview with Die Zeit newspaper in Germany, November 2019

Having found adults harder to convince, climate activists deliberately target children using fear-mongering tactics. A emphasis of anger and aggression and a desire to cancel out any who disagree with their version of "climate change" [i] is encouraged.

Today's youth are being indoctrinated from a young age with the theory of man-made climate change being taught across all age groups throughout the world's school systems. Secular environmentalists know this strategy works. The educational system has been effectively used to advance a secular worldview among young people. Thus making them more sympathetic to progressive social views including the ideas of socialism and Marxism.

Numerous extreme eco-terrorist[4] groups like Extinction Rebellion use and encourage naive teenagers to skip school in order to participate in "climate change protests". And radicalized teenage "youth leaders" are regularly used to speak and make demands at various conferences and at the United Nations.

I believe this targeting and using children is wrong in so many ways. The Bible admonishes parents to bring up their children in the way they should go.

"Teach them in their growing years with Christian teaching"
Ephesians 6:4 NLV

My hope is that this book will help parents to better understand the issues their children are facing. And be informed to teach them the truth.

---

[4] I believe the eco-terrorist label is accurate due to their tactics. They include industrial sabotage, physical attacks on those they oppose and mass civil disruptions that shut down businesses and cause financial loss to individuals caught up in the chaos they cause.

- Chapter 7: Indoctrinating young people, covers this in more detail

Truth #3: Climate change is a financial scam

The climate change industry is worth $trillions. Make no mistake, "green energy", electric vehicles, carbon capture technologies, plant based meat as well as the $billions in government funded research, grants and marketing $ is very good business. Fortunes are being made, often based on nothing but ideas and taxpayer-funded subsidies.

Take Al Gore for instance, the world's first carbon billionaire. Not one of his many climate change predictions over the last 20 years has come true. Yet this hasn't stopped him preaching his climate gospel and building a climate alarmist empire worth nearly $1billion dollars. All by investing in solutions to correct the problems he predicted that have never happened![ii, iii]

Likewise selling renewable energy systems has made many investors and companies very wealthy. And while solar energy is very useful for off-grid and emergency power systems, it's not true that renewable power is free, clean or good for the environment! Wind and solar power are actually expensive compared to nuclear, coal and gas powered energy systems. Germany is a good case study. After spending over $580 billion switching to renewable energy, German citizens now pay the highest energy costs in Europe. Plus they have regular blackouts and load shedding as their solar and wind powered energy grid struggles to keep up with the intermittent supply that comes from renewable power[iv]. To add insult to injury, German carbon emissions didn't go down after their switch to "renewables".[5] And they regularly import energy from neighboring countries.

In like manner, Californians have found out that their state's green energy policy is a disaster. They mandated unreliable green energy solutions, stopping the construction of abundant natural gas infrastructure and prematurely closing existing coal and nuclear power plants. California now has one of the most unstable and unreliable power grids in the nation. Regular blackouts don't however seem to matter to those in power, as they plan to close their last remaining nuclear power station. The simple fact is that California's energy policy is primarily concerned with following climate cult theology, rather providing stable power.

And as normally happens when governments decide to "invest" in unsound ideologically driven projects, we the people end up footing the bill via higher energy costs and taxes.

- Chapter 16: Renewable energy, covers this in more detail

---

[5] To clarify, I'm not totally against all renewable energy. I believe it's too expensive and most current forms are not reliable. Because of that, I don't believe it's the total solution we need right now, at least not for most modern economies. In the future however with better technology, especially in energy storage, it could be more viable.

Truth #4: Climate change is a danger to our freedom and a front for socialism

"It must be understood that what is occurring here, ... is the whole climate change process is a complete transformation of the economic structure of the world."

United Nations climate czar, Christina Figueres

Of great concern to anyone paying attention are the overwhelming socialist and Marxist views among most radical environmentalists. Former Czech president Vaclav Klaus, who lived under communism, boldly declared,

"Environmentalism is the new face of communism." He warns, *"It becomes evident that, while discussing the climate, we are not witnessing a clash of views about the environment, but a clash of views about human freedom."*

And this point is more dangerous than many realize. The climate change "crisis" is designed to create the sense of an emergency where none exists. Political leaders are already using this "threat" to raise taxes and curb freedoms. And if the 2020 coronavirus pandemic has taught us anything, it's that too many governmental leaders at all levels have more deep-rooted despotic tendencies than many would have ever believed and any "crisis" will be exploited.

If many of the big green social plans that many politicians are talking about are ever imposed, they will ultimately allow the government to gain almost total control of our lives! All of which will do nothing for the climate at all. And I'm talking about right here in the USA. Based on the actions and comments of most left leaning leaders, it's not difficult to understand the climate change agenda. It's about changing and controlling society via a mixture of radical Marxist and socialist ideas under the cover of going green. Consider the following statements:

"The interesting thing about the Green New Deal is it wasn't originally a climate thing at all," "Do you guys think of it as a climate thing?" "Because we really think of it as a how-do-you-change-the-entire-economy thing."[1]

Saikat Chakrabarti, one of the architects behind the New Green Deal and Social Democrat Rep. Alexandria Ocasio-Cortez's chief of staff in a conversation with the Washington Post

"No matter if the science is all phony, there are collateral environmental benefits. ... Climate change (provides) the greatest chance to bring about justice and equality in the world."

Christine Stewart, Canada's former Minister of the Environment, talking to editors and reporters of the *Calgary Herald*

And consider this December 2019 quotation from Swedish teenage activist Greta Thunberg:

"After all, the climate crisis is not just about the environment. It is a crisis of human rights, of justice, and of political will. Colonial, racist, and patriarchal systems of oppression have created and fueled it. We need to dismantle them all."

She didn't think this up on her own. She has been coached as a mouthpiece for the climate movement. The point that I am really passionately trying to convey is the longer-term goal for the climate change agenda is far more dangerous than most of us realize. The ultimate goal is the introduction of a socialist one-world government system under the auspices of the United Nations or similar global agency. The threat of global climate change is being used as a convenient front to gain control of vital industries, and increase the reliance of populations on governments.

Now I don't want to give the impression that all climate change activists are part of some huge conspiracy theory to usher in a one-world government and enslave us all. The large majority of climate change believers and promoters are caught up in something they don't fully understand. In other words they are deceived "useful idiots". They have drunk the Kool-Aid and are true believers in the cause. Many have good intentions and really think they are going to contribute to saving the planet. However, at higher levels of government and certainly in global institutions like the United Nations, many leaders openly admit that the climate change emergency is an opportunity for them to change society. Many are openly socialist and see the so-called "climate change emergency" as a way to advance their globalist agenda in the name of a coordinated global response. Which naturally would leave them in charge.

That's because the end game of promoting climate change is nothing other than a new world order, which would set the stage for the end time anti-Christ and his global government.

Here is Klaus Schwab, the founder and executive chairman of World Economic Forum, calling for a "global reset" in order for the world to be able to survive the next big global crisis, "climate change". [v]

"Every country, from the United States to China, must participate, and every industry, from oil and gas to tech, must be transformed. In short, we need a 'Great Reset' of capitalism." All in order to *"rebalance economies,"* promote *"fairness,"* and create greater *"equity" within societies and among nations."*

What does this have to do with climate change? The answer is simple; climate change is the scare tactic to get societies to enact the global agenda of a one-world government.

- Chapter 8: The climate change end game, covers this in more detail

Part 1: Understanding the climate cult

1. Establishing a base line

In order to debunk the misbeliefs surrounding climate change we need to first establish a case for the defense of truth, a baseline by which we can measure claims. So let's start with some facts and work from there.

It is claimed that climate change is the biggest crisis facing humanity today. That it's a clear danger to the future of life on earth. Consequently, the United Nations and many national governments have declared climate change an emergency. In reality what is meant is that the average temperature of the earth has risen ever so slightly over the last century. Some climate scientists have used this small rise to extrapolate and develop computerized climate models that show dramatic temperature increases over the remainder of this century and beyond. This fabricated future temperature is the so-called "climate change emergency". And scientifically challenged politicians, celebrities and protesters are hysterical about it. It's the bedrock claim upon which $billions have been spent on climate alarmist propaganda. It is now spread across thousands of websites, blogs and used in numerous docudramas. All created in order to protect the planet and some of us[6] from this terrible imagined future that most scientists don't even agree upon:

"The data doesn't matter. We're not basing our recommendations on the data. We're basing them on climate models"

Prof. Chris Folland, Hadley Centre for Climate Prediction and Research

"The (climate) models are convenient fictions that provide something very useful"

Dr. David Frame, climate modeler, Oxford University

To make it clear, there is some evidence that the "average temperature" at the earth's surface has increased by approximately 1°C/1.8°F since the pre-industrial period. Some argue more, some argue less. However, the slight amount of average warming is not the whole story. For that we need to go back in time to see what happened before the pre-industrial period. Doing so allows us to have intelligent conversations and put the climate change discussion in its right context, based on real, not imagined facts. This is covered in the next chapter.

It's also important to point out that it's not a simple task to measure and calculate the average temperature of the earth. It sounds easy but it's not. Measurements are combined from land, sea and satellite readings. Sensors above the earth's surface measure the air temperature in a particular location. Buoys measure sea temperatures, and in other places boats

---

[6] Not all of us, because part of the solution climate cult radicals propose to save the planet includes eliminating a large percentage of mankind.

actually lower thermometers into the sea for readings. Satellites provide lower tropospheric temperature data sets. These are added to the surface temperature data sets. After "error" correcting, an average temperature is calculated per grid box, which is an area on the map. All these numerous data sets are used, and each gets combined to calculate the average global temperature.

As to how accurate the global average temperature is, that's another story. While measurements today are no doubt far more accurate than they were even a quarter of a century ago, there is still lots of room for error. There is no standard for taking temperatures with different countries using different methods. There is also disagreement about the accuracy of satellite measurements in the presence of clouds and rain. An additional question is how easy would it be for actual errors or human bias "error" corrections to be included? I couldn't find any research or studies that take into account and balance any conformational bias in the data. Consider the general disagreements in almost every other area of science, and especially in the charged atmosphere of climate change. I certainly wouldn't rule out the possibility that some data sets are exaggerated. Bear this in mind the next time you hear some climate activist or politician making bold claims about future global temperatures.

2. The ever-changing climate

A timeline of the world's ever-changing climate

In the beginning of time as recorded in the historical account in Genesis, God describes what He was creating as "good", four separate times (Genesis 1: 10, 12, 18 & 25).

"Then God saw everything that He had made, and indeed it was very good."
Genesis 1:31

On the sixth day at the end of the creation week, God looked down on His complete creation and tells us that everything He made was **very good**[7]. Not only did all the individual parts from the smallest subatomic particles to the very largest created planets and galaxies work perfectly, but also the entire, integrated creation as a whole was in harmony. God specially recorded His view of the finished creation as "very good"; so that there could be no doubt that the original creation was not like the corrupted, sin plagued physical world we live in today.

---

[7] The word "good" in the original Hebrew text is "tov". Tov means in harmony. In other words, the original creation before sin entered into the world was in harmony, without death, disease, storms or natural disasters that we experience in the world today.

In the beginning

We know almost nothing about the climate of our earth when it was originally created, before sin entered the world. We do know however from Genesis 1:14 that there were different seasons that God created as part of the natural cycle of the earth.

"Then God said, "Let lights appear in the sky to separate the day from the night. Let them be signs to mark the seasons, days, and years."

And the tilt of the earth, which is currently at an angle of 23.4367°, helps maintain the seasons. As earth orbits the sun at this angle, different parts of our planet are closer to the sun at different times of the year. The pole tilted towards the sun is in summer, while the opposite pole tilted away from the sun is in its winter period.

This axial tilt could be as God originally designed it. Or it could have been altered during the upheaval that split the continents apart when the world was flooded, during the time of Noah. We have no way to know for sure. What we do know however is that part of the covenant promise God made to Noah, after the floodwaters had receded, was a promise that the different seasons would continue.

"As long as the earth remains, there will be planting and harvest, cold and heat, summer and winter, day and night". Genesis 8:22 NLT

Sin changed everything

It's difficult for most non-believers to understand, but the physical world we currently inhabit, is not how it was originally created. It's also certainly not functioning as God, the designer and creator intended it to. So what happened? How did our natural world end up producing massive hurricanes, killer tornadoes, earth splitting and building destroying earthquakes, and deadly snowstorms?

The short answer is, sin changed everything! The creation came under a curse when Adam sinned. We are living in a sin cursed world where death, disease, decay and natural disasters are seen all around us. This is a spiritual problem that will only be resolved when Jesus returns. While we are spiritually saved by the redemptive work of the cross, we still live in physical bodies on a physical earth that is still under the curse of sin. Numerous passages in the Bible explain this:

"And to Adam He said, Because you have listened and given heed to the voice of your wife and have eaten of the tree of which I commanded you, saying, You shall not eat of it, the ground is under a curse because of you; in sorrow and toil shall you eat [of the fruits] of it all the days of your life. Thorns also and thistles shall it bring forth for you, and you shall eat the plants of the field. In the sweat of your face shall you eat bread until you return to the ground, for out of it you were taken; for dust you are and to dust you shall return."
Genesis 3:17-19

"Against its will, all creation was subjected to God's curse. But with eager hope, the creation looks forward to the day when it will join God's children in glorious freedom from death and decay."
Romans 8: 20-21 NLT

"The earth mourns and dries up, and the land wastes away and withers. Even the greatest people on earth waste away. The earth suffers for the sins of its people, for they have twisted God's instructions, violated His laws, and broken His everlasting covenant. Therefore, a curse consumes the earth."
Isaiah 24:4 -6a

In the New King James Version of Isaiah 24:6 it reads like this, *"Therefore the curse has devoured the earth."* Note it's the curse of sin that consumes and devours the earth. Not fossil fueled powered cars and planes! Even though they may spew out some pollution, they are not the root cause. The curse on the physical world is a direct result of mankind's rebellion against God the creator. Furthermore Isaiah 14: 16-18, talking about satan, records *" Is this the one who destroyed the world and made it into a wasteland?"* Note the Bible says that the devil turned the world into a wasteland, via the curse.

The good news is all of creation will be set free from the curse it endured when Jesus returns to earth.

"For all creation is waiting eagerly for that future day when God will reveal who his children really are. Against its will, all creation was subjected to God's curse. But with eager hope, the creation looks forward to the day when it will join God's children in glorious freedom from death and decay. For we know that all creation has been groaning as in the pains of childbirth right up to the present time. And we believers also groan, even though we have the Holy Spirit within us as a foretaste of future glory, for we long for our bodies to be released from sin and suffering. We, too, wait with eager hope for the day when God will give us our full rights as his adopted children, including the new bodies he has promised us. We were given this hope when we were saved."
Romans 8:19 – 24

Climate before the flood

As the Bible doesn't tell us a lot about the pre-flood world, a degree of educated speculation will always be involved in any weather or climate discussion of this period. This is my best attempt at a reasonable conclusion using the facts we have.

The fossil record clearly shows larger versions of animal types than those of the ones that exist today, (which are much smaller). This includes giant scorpions, ammonites, centipedes, sharks, crocodiles and snakes. Even fossilized dragonflies have been found that are as large as today's eagles. These and numerous other types of animals have all been found preserved in fossilized form. Their pre-flood, large size clearly indicates a warmer, and more oxygen rich environment. From this we can conclude that the weather and climate were very different before the global flood in the time of Noah, which shaped the earth into what we see today.

The canopy

It is assumed by many Biblical scholars that there was a canopy of some sort that covered the earth.

In Genesis 1:6 we read of "the waters above the firmament". The Hebrew word for "firmament", (or "expanse", as it is alternatively translated), is commonly believed to refer to the earth's atmosphere.

Many Bible scholars believe there was a canopy over the earth. This protected the pre-flood world from the harmful effects of the sun. And which could have allowed for higher oxygen levels. This could have contributed to the larger size of pre-flood animals, which we only know from their fossilized remains today. It's possible that the pre-flood canopy was made from water vapor, and during the flood, it collapsed or rained down as recorded in Genesis

"In the six hundredth year of Noah's life, in the second month, the seventeenth day of the month, on that day all the fountains of the great deep were broken up, and the windows of heaven were opened. And the rain was on the earth forty days and forty nights."
Genesis 7:11-12

There was a time before it rained on the earth

"When the Lord God made the earth and the heavens, neither wild plants nor grains were growing on the earth. For the Lord God had not yet sent rain to water the earth, and there were no people to cultivate the soil. Instead, springs came up from the ground and watered all the land."
Genesis 2: 4-6

Plants were watered from water springs and, or water vapor mist. Some Bible scholars argue that this was only in the period before God made man, and then it rained afterwards. Well if you believe in a young earth, as I do, that would be on the 6th day, so I personally don't subscribe to the "mist-was-only-before-God-created-man" theory. The more plain reading indicates that there was no rain until the global flood of Noah. Additionally, we have the fact that God used a rainbow after the flood. Today the rainbow is a naturally occurring phenomenon when light passes through raindrops. It's a symbol that He will never totally flood the whole earth again. It also supports the theory that it had not rained up until the time of the flood, as seeing a rainbow was something new to Noah.

So no rain would have meant far less or possibly no wind at all, no rain clouds or storms, no thunder and lightening, no sleet, hail or snow at all before the time of Noah. Therefore all in all, the world and its climate before the flood were probably very different from what we experience today post-flood.

The climate after the flood

"Then God told Noah and his sons, "I hereby confirm my covenant with you and your descendants, and with all the animals that were on the boat with you—the birds, the livestock, and all the wild animals—every living creature on earth. Yes, I am confirming my covenant with you. Never again will floodwaters kill all living creatures; never again will a flood destroy the earth."
Genesis 9:8-11 NLT

Noah and his family and all the land animals found a very different world and weather when they exited the Ark. Instead of a single landmass, the world had literally been torn apart during the flood and the continental landmasses we see today were created. The world also had several new large oceans. There were massive mountain ranges that didn't previously exist. There were probably many active land based volcanoes[8]. And there were strong winds and rainstorms caused by the new weather systems and lastly something totally new; snow and ice.

---

[8] During the flood, intense volcanic activity occurred when the ground and earth's crust was ripped apart as new oceans formed between the continents as they are today. These undersea volcanoes are seen on all ocean floors around the tectonic plates.

During the flood massive amounts of volcanic ash filled the skies. This would have blocked out sunlight from large areas of the earth for years, possibly for several decades. This combined with still warm oceans from the volcanic activity during the flood caused evaporation, which in turn fell as snow and formed ice. As the snow fell, large glaciers were formed and the Ice Age period began.

The Roman Warm Period (250 BC to 400 AD)

Jumping forward in time, let's pick up in the time of the Roman Empire and the aptly named Roman Warm Period that occurred from around 250 BC to 400 AD.

Many today have tried to play down or erase the Roman Warm Period from history as it challenges their theory that the earth is warmer today than ever before. And that warming is caused by industrial activity. Neither of these statements are entirely true. There are literally hundreds of scientific and historical records published from studies all over Europe that attest to the warmer temperatures of the Roman Warm Period[vi],[vii].

A few historical facts confirm the much warmer weather in Europe during the time of the Roman Empire. Firstly Hannibal, the Carthaginian General who crossed the European Alps to attack Rome (in modern day Italy). He made his journey on African elephants in the winter of 218 BC. Anyone who has visited the Alps in the winter knows there is no way you could do that today due to the huge amount of snow and ice. Studies from this time show no record of even any frost in parts of the Alps, confirming that Hannibal and his army were able to make one of the most daring military raids of all time.

And in 50 BC Julius Caesar had to build bridges to cross the fast flowing Rhine River. After he retreated he destroyed the bridges, letting the Rhine act as a natural barrier to keep Germanic tribes at bay even during the winter[viii]. However, in 406 AD, the winter was once again cold enough to freeze the river so that the Vandals could simply walk over the frozen ice and attack the Romans[9],[10].

Lastly consider the way the Romans dressed most of the time. There are many sites where Roman uniforms have been recovered. Their clothing wasn't exactly what anyone would consider warm weather gear fit for living in Northern Europe, year round.

The Medieval Warm Period (900 to 1300 AD)

Several centuries after the Roman Warm Period came to an end, another multi-century period of warming, the Medieval Warm Period (MWP) occurred. This transpired during the European Middle Ages, from approximately 900 to 1300 AD. Historical records give us lots to work from and record extreme warm weather during this time. Temperatures were believed to be at least 1-2°C/1.8-3.6°F above today's temperatures and there are reports of even up to 3°C /5.4°F warmer weather in Northern Europe. This usually warmer climate is what enabled the Vikings to expand their world as their voyages to Iceland and Greenland were seldom hindered by ice during this time.

---

[9] This didn't occur during the reign of Julius Caesar, as the warm winter weather didn't freeze the fast flowing Rhine River.

[10] The Vandals were one of a number of "barbarian" tribes blamed for the fall of the Roman Empire.

In the summer of 1130 AD, it was so dry in what is today the western part of Germany that you could literally wade through the Rhine River. Today large boats navigate the same waterways. Likewise in 1135 AD the water flow in the Danube (Europe's second longest river) was so low that people could cross it on foot. For much of recorded history, right up to today, the Danube has acted as a major commercial highway between the nations it flows through, carrying large boatloads of people and goods. Only a major prolonged drought caused by much drier and warmer than our current weather, could dry up these mighty rivers. With the end of the Medieval Warm Period the heyday of the Vikings ended.

The Little Ice Age (1300 – 1800s AD)

After the Medieval Warm Period, the world's climate transitioned from a period of great heat to one of great cold. This cooling period came to be known as the Little Ice Age (LIA). Scholars debate the exact dates but it occurred from around 1300 AD to the late 1800s. This period coincided with lower solar sun spot [11] activity, which typically corresponds with colder temperatures on the earth. Between 1645 AD and 1715 AD a prolonged period of low solar activity occurred. During this time the coldest periods of the Little Ice Age occurred. This grand solar minimum period was known as the Maunder Minimum.

_____

[11] Sunspots are seen as fiery disks on the surface of the sun. They are highly magnetized, and shoot out solar flares. These magnetic explosions blast our earth with flashes of extreme ultraviolet radiation. In general, periods with lower sunspot activity have corresponded with cooler temperatures being recorded on the earth.

Some scholars disagree that solar activity alone produced the extreme colder weather and suggest that higher volcanic activity created ash clouds that blocked out much of the sun's radiation and reduced temperatures around the globe. Either way, there are hundreds of historical records of extreme cold, ice and lots of snow even during some summer months. Painters of the time recorded this period in their now historical works showing ice-skaters on rivers and severe winter landscapes with deeper than usual snow, some even in locations where snow today is rare. This time of extreme cold and food shortage is attributed to being one of the causes leading up to the French Revolution in the 1790's.

Numerous historical records detail the River Thames in London frozen solid throughout the summer. Likewise the Baltic Sea froze over, which enabled the Swedes to march across and invade Denmark. Around 1550 AD the Vikings abandoned their settlements in Greenland as nothing could grow in the frozen ground. Today many of their former burial places are still found in the frozen Greenland permafrost[12]. In like manner many higher elevation villages throughout Europe were abandoned as year round snow made living there impossible.

Today many climate change proponents ignore the fact that temperatures during this period were so much colder than usual. They deceitfully point out in numerous climate charts how temperatures have "risen" from this time period without explaining that the weather was not normal but actually freezing cold so temperatures were returning back to the more even temperatures we experience today.

---

[12] Permafrost is perennially frozen ground. It forms in areas where the annual air temperature is below freezing, 0°C / 32°F.

Re-writing history

Just like the Truth Ministry in George Orwell's novel 1984, both the United Nations Intergovernmental Panel on Climate Change (IPCC) and numerous climate scientists are actively engaged in trying to erase or at the very least, reconstruct the climatic data from both the Medieval Warm Period and the Little Ice Age. This is being done by editing out any mention of these periods in academic curriculum, adjusting computer climate models, and redrawing average temperature weather graphs to lessen the impact of both these periods.

At the same time, an Internet search campaign is being waged to fill search results with articles and links to minimize both periods. Some climate change activists even flat out deny they existed at all. Their efforts are reminiscent of authoritarian governments and religious cults throughout history, who have tried to re-write history books by destroying all materials that don't line up with their version of the truth.

However, it's hard to deny all the archeological evidence and historical accounts of events. Over 700 different scientists have published papers covering the Medieval Warm Period alone ensuring there is more than historical evidence to support this warmer than usual period.

20th century cooling

During the last century and prior to 1980, the global average temperature was mostly stable or dropping. This led previous generations of climate scientists in the 1970s to argue the case for "global cooling". At the time, Time Magazine and other mass publications all carried cover stories promoting the global cooling theory and predicting a new ice age.

"Telltale signs are everywhere – from the unexpected persistence and thickness of pack ice in the waters around Iceland to the southward migration of a warmth-loving creature like the armadillo from the Midwest. Since the 1940s the mean global temperature has dropped about 2.7⁰ F"

Time Magazine article, "Another Ice Age", June 24, 1974

The 20ᵗʰ century lukewarm period

From the early 1980s to around mid 1990s there was a short period when temperatures actually rose, by approximately 1° C / 1.8° F. Jumping on this slight increase and modeling future predicted temperature increases is what has led to the current global warming / climate change hysteria.

Even worse, in an attempt to categorize the slight increase in temperature as part of a bigger, long-term trend, climate researchers have tried to erase or minimize The Little Ice Age (LIA). Claiming it either didn't happen, or it wasn't really very cold, or it only occurred over a small part of the earth, or some combination of all three combined[ix]. By reducing the cooling impact of the LIA, and reconstructing temperature models, they ignore that global temperatures were starting from a cold point at the end of the 1800s. Doing so they try to show the small rise of the last century not as a return to normal, but rather as an "increase due to industrial activity" and hay presto, "man-made global warming / climate change" was magically produced!

The present time pause

"Observations do not show rising temperatures throughout the tropical troposphere ... This is just downright dangerous."

Professor Peter Thorne, climatologist Hadley Centre for Climate Prediction and Research, Met Office, UK (2007)

Around 1997, the slight warming of the 20th century stopped. Numerous leading climate change promoters begrudgingly confirmed this.

"The UN's climate change chief, Rajendra Pachauri, has acknowledged a 17-year pause in global temperature rises, confirmed recently by Britain's Met Office, but said it would need to last 30 to 40 years at least to break the long-term global warming trend." [x]

In an attempt to ignore the failings of their own computer models and predictions, climate scientists now claim we are currently in a semi-stable "pause" or "plateau" period where warming has stopped but will soon resume. Many climate scientists are even baffled, especially as CO_2 concentrations in the atmosphere have continued to rise. Some of the more honest now admit their computerized climate forecast models, which predicted continued rising temperatures were wrong.

Professor Kevin Trenberth, climate scientist and the lead author of the 2001 and 2007 IPCC Scientific Assessment of Climate Change reports, confirmed in 2009 that there was in fact, no current warming. And he didn't know why. This was a shock to him, as all his models showed there would be warming:

"The fact is that we can't account for the lack of warming at the moment and it is a travesty that we can't."

Kevin Trenberth, expert climate scientist and author of over 560 scientific papers and 47 books

And as the years have rolled by since even the slightest increase in global temperatures were reported, it was obvious to everyone that global warming was in serious trouble. What's the use of global warming if the weather is not getting warmer? So a name change was needed and global warming became climate change. *(See section on marketing climate change for info on the "climate change name game".)* Now with climate change even if the global average temperature didn't increase, well it was because of climate change. This is rather convenient!

Some honest climate scientists now admit they got it wrong. Here is Dr. John Christly presenting testimony to Congress and demonstrating that the UN IPCC climate models grossly exaggerated the risk of climate change:

"The models over-warmed the tropical atmosphere by a factor of approximately three"

Dr. John Christly, before Congress, February 2016

In yet another report, Professor Myles Allen from Oxford University who also writes for the UN IPCC, admitted the climate models used to predict climate change are wrong;

"We haven't seen the rapid acceleration in warming after 2000 that we see in the models. We haven't seen that in the observations"

Professor Myles Allen, head of the Climate Dynamics Group at Oxford University and co-author of the 2018 UN IPCC climate change report

And they are not the only former UN climate change experts who now disagree with the UN's official position. Professor Yuri Izrael, former vice president of the UN IPCC clearly states:[1]

"There is no proven link between human activity and global warming at all."

In other words, the UN IPCC got it so wrong we should throw out their incorrect predictions. However, instead of being impartial, many of the political class and their supporters in the media simply ignored these and numerous other reports showing that climate change data predictions are total fiction.

And since announcing that no new warming could be found, in an attempt to keep the climate change ball rolling, the more radical climate change believing scientists have tried many times to redraw charts and change the way they interpret the data. All in order to claim "silly us, there was no pause, we made a mistake, climate change is still valid and it's getting warmer". That is the way this works. They manipulate data, deceive, lie, and cover up in order to protect the climate change narrative[xi].

Fortunately not all governments have been prepared to go along with the climate change myth. Japan, in a break from most other industrialized nations, announced in 2018 that they would be building 35 new coal power plants. The Japanese Meteorological Agency confirmed that in their opinion there is no current global warming. Prime minister Abe declared,

"For the past three decades, there has been no significant warming in any major Japanese cities at all."[xii]

3. The climate cult

"We're not going to stop. The earth's not waiting. It's just heating up. And it's on fire"

Activist group Extinction Rebellion organizer Dave Robinson, promising more disruptions at a protest in Denver, October 2019 [xiii]

Worshiping the planet

The modern secular environmental movement is an example of the twisted thinking that occurs when people reject God and a Biblical worldview.

The passion of many climate change activists is an outward expression of the quasi-religious nature of the modern environmental movement. A mixture of secular atheism and pagan environmentalism has filled the void created by the rejection of traditional Christianity among many younger people. The result is radical environmentalism has become a form of religion for atheists and others who reject God.

Extreme environmentalism has morphed into an upside down movement where nature and natural resources must be preserved at all costs. So instead of sensible conservation and stewardship, with nature preserved for the future benefit and the enjoyment of mankind, we are often treated as the enemy of the planet. Radical environmentalists speak of "preserving the purity of nature" and demanding "ecological justice". In other words, the natural world has become an idol to them. "Mother Earth"[13] in a sense is treated as some kind of capricious goddess who releases hurricanes, wildfires, pandemics and earthquakes to punish or take revenge on those who harm the environment.

"Mother Earth is angry. She's telling us, whether she is telling us with hurricanes on the Gulf Coast, fires in the west, whatever it is, that the climate crisis is real and has an impact." xiv

House speaker Nancy Pelosi (D-California), September 11, 2020

This view of course is totally opposite of what the Bible teaches.

"But God made the earth by His power; He founded the world by His wisdom and stretched out the heavens by His understanding. When He thunders, the waters in the heavens roar; He makes clouds rise from the ends of the earth. He sends lightning with the rain and brings out the wind from his storehouses."
Jeremiah 10:12 -13

The Word of God is full of similar references. No, the earth is not a living being that displays emotion and it's certainly never to be treated as such or worshiped in any way whatsoever.

---

[13] The earliest historical references to "Mother Earth" are found in Greek manuscripts from 12 or 13 BC.

A brief history of the radical environmental movement

"We the human species, are confronting a planetary emergency-a threat to the survival of our civilization that is gathering ominous and destructive potential...the earth has a fever. And the fever is rising...Indeed, without realizing it, we have begun to wage war on earth itself."

Al Gore, Ex Vice President who has made hundreds of $millions selling the myth of climate change

Since the beginning of time, mankind has been fascinated with and studied the natural world. The Greeks in particular started a systemic philosophical study of nature and natural history. In the mid 1800s when the first zoos began to appear in major cities people began to be exposed to wildlife from beyond their local region.

In the United States, wildlife was abundant when the first pioneers moved westwards. It wasn't until the 2nd half of the 19th century, from 1850 onwards with the expansion of the country through railways, and the development of new cities and roads, that people started to notice that many species of wildlife had started to become scarce. In the early 20th century the first wildlife conservation laws were passed when Theodore Roosevelt established the U.S. Forest Service. He also created the first national wildlife refuge and passed laws that made the hunting of migratory birds (except waterfowl) illegal. If it wasn't for the admirable actions of foresighted conservation pioneers like Theodore Roosevelt and others, the world would have lost many more species of wildlife through overhunting and habitat lose.

In wasn't however until April 22, 1970, when the first Earth Day celebration and protests took place that the general public was introduced to environmental concerns as political issues and the modern environmental movement was born.

From the very beginning, the two broad goals of the environmental movement were to (a) conserve wildlife and (b) to preserve the environment. Both were commendable and much needed goals. Sensible conservation is important and good. Few would argue with that. However, over the years within the environmental movement, the focus has shifted from conservation of nature to benefit mankind, to nature and environmental rights that too often see mankind as the enemy of the natural world. Mostly socialist and Marxist leaning academics have driven this shift in outlook. For years no-one really paid attention as the world's universities and education systems moved progressively leftwards. Currently much of the environmental movement today holds radical views on most social issues, including seeing humans as subservient to the environment.

"Phasing out the human race will solve every problem on earth, social and environmental."

David Foreman, founder of radical environmentalist group, Earth First!

Environmental Rights

With the best of intentions, most environmental conservation efforts started out by saving natural habitats and wildlife for future generations to enjoy. However, this type of good conservation has now morphed into the planet-first, antihuman movement we see today. The current push for environmental rights is a continuation of this secular trend that places the creation first.

Environmental lawyers are seeking to have land, rivers and other environmental features treated the same way as people[xv]. And in many places they are succeeding. Basic human rights have now been extended to include legal personhood rights being granted to everything from rivers to volcanoes.

Any sane person knows that trees, mountains and even animals are not a legal person, and they are not capable of understanding or enjoying the rights of a human being. Yet this hasn't stopped environmental extremists from pushing for, and in many cases getting these legal rights granted. In 2008, Ecuador became the first country to enshrine the rights of nature into their constitution, allowing eco-systems to be named a defendant to protect themselves. In 2017 a river in New Zealand was recognized as a legal person. Environmentalist groups are working to establish similar rights for the many other physical natural features, wildlife and eco-systems worldwide[xvi].

The spirit of the anti-Christ

"For many deceivers have gone out into the world, those who do not acknowledge Jesus Christ as coming in the flesh. This is the deceiver and the anti-Christ."
2 John 1:7

Behind any worldview that doesn't recognize God as the creator and Jesus as Lord is the demonic spirit of the anti-Christ. And anything that diverts worship away from God and His stated purposes is demonic in its origin. Modern environmentalism and climate change is no different. This can be seen from its focus on creation, not the Creator. The agenda is antihuman, pro-environment.

Isaiah 5:20 warns of this kind of wrong thinking, declaring, *"You are headed for trouble! You say wrong is right, darkness is light, and bitter is sweet."* This is a snapshot of the thinking behind much radical environmental and climate change rhetoric today as the examples throughout the book show.

Climate cult theology

Just like other environment scares before it, climate change has developed its own theology and is promoted much like a false religion.

Climate cult scientists act as FALSE PROPHETS, predicting the future and creating fear. They spread a message of a future coming APOCALYPSE unless their pronouncements and solutions are accepted. Their every word is believed and hung onto by their followers, scientifically challenged politicians, celebrities and journalists.

The world's major media outlets are the mouthpieces of the climate cult. They manipulate facts and routinely publish climate exaggerations as FALSE PASTORS preaching a message of future doom. All the while demonizing anyone who disagrees with them.

Radical professors, teachers and academics are FALSE TEACHERS who propagandize their students in schools and universities. There are literally hundreds of websites and organizations producing climate change materials for teachers. UNESCO (United Nations Educational, Scientific and Cultural Organization) lists the teaching of climate change to young people as one of its main goals[xvii].

Many celebrities, actors and entertainers use their huge global star-power like FALSE EVANGELISTS, spreading the message via propaganda documentaries and their huge social media followings. They have influenced massive numbers of people around the globe.

Just like any cult, secular climate change zealots even have their own online confessional courtesy of NBC News where you can CONFESS your climate sins [xviii].

Any climate change scientist who doesn't agree with climate cult theology risks EX-COMMUNICATION, via losing their job and funding and having their social media accounts and comments censored or canceled.

In one of the most blatant examples of censoring dissenting views, Mike Shellenberger, himself a green environmentalist with impeccable leftist credentials, wrote an article in Forbes, debunking some of the worst examples of climate alarmism, positions he once embraced. It didn't take long though for Forbes magazine to cave to pressure from extreme climate cult activists and take down his opinion piece, *"I apologize for the climate scare."* [xix] YouTube likewise did the same with Michael Moore's film, *Planet of the Humans*, removing it from their platform because he spoke out against the renewable energy industry[14]. Deplatforming is rapidly becoming the new cancel culture censorship tool of choice for leftist radicals who are not prepared to debate anyone who disagrees with their ideology.

And lastly untold millions of DEVOTEES around the world blindly support and follow their leaders, many protesting and demanding "action" with a religious zeal.

---

[14] After much public criticism, YouTube reversed their decision and allowed the film back on their platform. If Moore was a conservative however, it's doubtful YouTube would have changed their decision.

Anyone who disagrees with them is persecuted with religious like fervor.

Climate change activism

"Activism is a way for people to feel important, even if the consequences of their activism are counterproductive for those they claim to be helping and damaging to the fabric of society as a whole."

Prof. Thomas Sowell, social theorist and economist, Stanford University

Climate change activism has become a form of self-righteousness for many. We see this in celebrities vying for attention to be seen, at least in public, as caring about the environment. Yet they fly around the world on private jets, live in over-sized, energy hogging mega mansions and out consume everyone else, all the while preaching to regular people, that they should "downsize" their lifestyles. They exemplify double standards of hypocrisy much like the Pharisees and Scribes did in Biblical times.

"Climate change is the greatest threat to our existence in our short history on this planet. Nobody's going to buy their way out of its effects."

Activist actor Mark Ruffalo

Radical environmental activist groups are the energy behind evangelizing the climate change cult. Their movement thrives on a false sense of emergency. In order to gain traction, eco-scare scenarios are regularly manufactured to create a sense of crisis. Environmentalist groups have successfully used these tactics for years to move their agenda forward. And it works for them. Organizing public protests, hunger strikes and generally disrupting other people's lives in an attempt to promote their cause. Some of the most radical groups have even called for martyrs willing to commit public suicide as a way to gain attention to their cause.[xx] According to David Rose of the Scottish Mail, in an article entitled *"Climate crazies plan 'public suicides' at next UN climate summit"*, climate activists are looking for 'extreme' ways to draw attention, including encouraging hunger strikes until death. In a leaked document they state, *"We need to go to extremes of sacrifice levels."*

The current disruption tactics of eco-radicals include:

- Public protests often supported by well-meaning but ill informed celebrities
- Blocking traffic and freeways
- Closing down airports with drones or protests
- Blockading government offices and businesses they don't agree with
- Disrupting political meetings
- Naked protests in major international cities
- Hunger strikes
- Classroom and workplace walk-outs
- Gluing themselves to the doors of buildings and in airports
- General public disruptions and loud protests all around the globe

Climate activists have a variety of ecological, social and political goals, they can be boiled down to saving the planet by banning all industrial activity they deem harmful. These would include: mining, anything that causes carbon emissions, stopping nearly all modern farming, most modern transportation and the majority of industrial industry.

Typical examples of the vague demands radicals insist on:

- Insisting governments declare a "global climate and ecological emergency"
- Banning all oil, gas and fossil fuel usage in order to make industry "carbon neutral" and reduce "greenhouse gas emissions to net zero" by some random future date
- Insisting governments "halt biodiversity loss"
- Demanding "climate and ecological justice" typically led by "citizen assemblies" or some other unelected group
- Only supporting politicians who will support all their demands

In other words, they have a utopian view of a wild and untouched natural planet, without most modern and industrial products or processes, ruled by progressive socialist governments. The wonderland most radical environmentalists "demand" doesn't actually exist. Their unrealistic goals can never be achieved. Most radicals don't understand that they use cars, trains, and fly on planes. They buy food from supermarkets or online and expect it to be delivered, and they live in an online social media virtual world that wouldn't exist if their "demands" were met. The only way to ever "get back" to their utopia, would mean wiping out most of the world's population, (many of whom would die of cold, heat or hunger) while destroying our modern world and economy. Most are painfully unaware of world and political history. They have no understanding that the socialist paradise they desire, once it became fully established wouldn't tolerate their public protests never mind anyone disrupting industry or disagreeing with official government policy.

Unfortunately many elected leaders don't understand the economic reality of what the protesting, and occasionally rioting, mobs are demanding either. For example, we have the

Los Angeles Mayor, Eric Garcetti encouraging and congratulating thousands of disrupting protesters in his city for "supporting the New Green Deal".

"It is time for us to have our 100% zero emission buildings, our 100% zero emission electricity and our 100% zero emission transportation," he said. *"That is our goal. Nothing less."[xxi]*

And while many extreme environmentalist groups currently adopt disruptive nuisance tactics, the long-term trend of the most radical is trending towards more violence[xxii, xxiii] . Intolerance abounds not only in society as a whole, but more so in radical environmentalist circles. An attitude of, "I'm right and if you don't agree with me, I will shout you down, boycott your business and blacklist you", is widely seen. And if that doesn't work, the more rabid activists are willing to use mob aggression tactics of violence, vandalism and sabotage against those involved in businesses they deem in opposition to their agenda. The industries they most often target include; energy, oil and gas, transportation, cars, farming and the meat industry.

Another manufactured crisis

"The only way to get our society to truly change is to frighten people with the possibility of a catastrophe."

Daniel Botkin, Emeritus Professor of Ecology, UC Santa Barbara

"On behalf of environmentalists, I apologize for the climate scare."

Michael Shellenberger, Time Magazine "Hero of the Environment," president of Environmental Progress

What is not well known is that many of the same scientists warning us about climate change now, were warning the world about global cooling not that long ago. They were proven wrong then and they are totally wrong now!

Climate cult radicals should understand that environmentalists and climate scientists have a long history of predicting calamity, with a corresponding poor record of accuracy. For years we have been told we are going to suffer and possibly perish from one catastrophic environmental event or another. And the major media outlets exaggerate every environmental issue because ratings and viewers matter more to them than accuracy. Yet none of these terrible, scary events have occurred. Or if they did in part, the consequences were not nearly as bad as predicted. Mankind is still here and life goes on. And it will continue to until Jesus returns.

A history of faulty predictions

Here is just a small sample of the scary environmental predictions that have proven to be either totally overblown or entirely false:

Dire famines will kill millions by 1975
As reported by numerous news outlets in 1967
* No famines occurred

Another Ice Age is coming fast
Reported in Time Magazine and almost every major news outlet promoting global cooling, in the mid 1970s
* No new ice age occurred

America will be subject to <u>water and food rationing</u> by 1980
Dr. Paul R Ehrlich, October 1970

- There was no food or water rationing
- Dr. Ehrlich is famous for his numerous false apocalyptic predictions regarding the world's population. Today he continues to be widely quoted by radical environmentalists and academics despite his poor track record

The greatest peril to life is <u>ozone depletion</u>
As reported by Time Magazine and almost every major news outlet, 1974

- An international effort banned most chlorofluorocarbons (CFCs) and this slowed some of the depletion. However, activist scientists still continue to make the same claims even though it's widely accepted that ozone levels change naturally with the seasons

<u>Acid rain</u> predicted to decimate the environment
Widely reported throughout the 1970s and 80s

- Several costly to industry clean air schemes were put in place. After spending more than half-billion-dollars over 10 years, the National Acid Precipitation Assessment Program study concluded that the clean air legislation had given us cleaner air. However, it also concluded acidity levels in many lakes was probably natural anyway and not the result of acid rain!

Massive droughts and sea levels rising at least 6 feet during the 1990s
James Hansen, NASA scientist alarmist during congressional testimony, 1988

- Totally wrong. Never happened. Yet James Hansen is seen as a hero for predicting global warming, which he continues to do
- Environmentalists continue to make sea level predictions of 6 – 12 feet or more. Yet there is scant evidence of any real sea levels rising
  - For more information on this subject, see chapter 14: Sea levels and climate change

Killer bee swarms will invade the USA
Reported from the 1970s through the end of the 1980s

- The bees did arrive, however they were less aggressive than predicted. They also hybridized with local honeybees, so they ended up as no problem

The Maldives will be underwater within 30 years
First reported in 1988

- Today over 30 years later not one of the 1,196 small Maldives islands is underwater

Peak oil predicted, with the world running out of oil by 2020
Richard Smalley, Noble Laureate in Chemistry, 1996

- It's 2020 and the world actually has greater proven oil reserves than at any other time in history[15]

---

[15] Oil reserves are actually a great case in point. New extraction technology advances have created an unforeseen economic boom and abundance of supply, making oil cheaper. If climate alarmists weren't so pessimistic they

Snow to disappear. Within a few years, children won't know what snow is
Most major news outlets reporting in 2000 and beyond. And in 2006 Al Gore predicted that Mt. Kilimanjaro, located just 205 miles from the equator would be snow free by 2016

- Today Mt. Kilimanjaro is still snow and ice capped all year round
- Another global warming false prediction. This last year has seen record snowfalls in numerous countries and including a record snowfall in Colorado in mid June[xxiv]

The bird flu/ H5N1 pandemic predicted to wipe out most of humanity
September 2005

- In 2013, the WHO (World Health Organization) reported there were 630 cases and 375 human deaths since 2003

Within 10 years sea levels will rise six meters due to the melting of Antarctic and Greenland ice sheets
Al Gore, 2007

- Like every climate change prediction Al Gore ever made, this one was wrong as well. There is more Antarctic sea ice today than ever
- Sea levels haven't risen at all

The Artic will be ice-free within 5 to 10 years
James Hansen, NASA scientist, 2008

- Another failed climate change prediction. The Artic Sea loses ice in the summer but gains it back

---

should learn a lesson, the same type of innovation will solve any real environment problem.

in the winter. Some years there is more ice, some years there is less

Flesh eating bacteria scare
In most major media channels during June, July & August 2019
- Reports go back to at least the 5th century
- Every few years the media jump on the story but cases are still extremely rare

Loss of Biodiversity will lead to extinction of mankind
Reported from 2015 onwards
- This scare is still trying to gain traction in the media. There is no credible science to this at all. Many scientists argue the opposite is occurring with more new species being discovered each year than reported lost
  - o For more information on this subject, see chapter 15: Plant and animal extinctions

"Murder hornets"
- At the time of writing "Murder hornets" [16] made a brief appearance in the media, with National Geographic, Newsweek, USAToday all headlining the story.
- However, after just a few months, the story has gone cold, at least for now

The next big eco-scare
Coming soon, watch this space. The media and entertainment industry are highly creative; we won't have to wait long!

---

[16] Asian giant hornet *(Vespa mandarinia)* is the world's largest hornet species. They are native to parts of South & Eastern Asia.

And while the list of terrible things that were meant to kill us or destroy the planet is very long, mankind is actually thriving and living longer than ever despite all the warnings. So why should we listen to a collective group who have never been totally accurate with their predictions? As is obvious from this list of false alerts, the environmental movement and most of the media thrive on presenting very worst-case scenarios. Big eco-scares are a staple part of their standard operating procedure. Climate change for the most part is another in a long list of made-up emergencies.

Even some environmentalists now admit that the scary climate change predictions have been overdone. Michael Shellenberger has been involved in environmental causes for over 25 years. After recognizing that many people are no longer listening to the obviously erroneous predictions that climate scientists churn out, he wrote an excellent book, *Apocalypse Never: Why environmentalism alarmism hurts us all,* exposing the many fallacies of climate change and the environmentalist movement.

Some of his highlights include:
- The most important thing for reducing air pollution and carbon emissions is moving from wood to coal to petroleum to natural gas to uranium
- Vegetarianism reduces one's emissions by less than 4%
- 100% renewables would require increasing the land used for energy from today's 0.5% to 50%

Many scientists and environmentalists are afraid to speak out for fear of losing their positions and friends. Michael Shellenberger admits as much:

"I remained quiet about the climate disinformation campaign because I was afraid of losing friends and funding. The few times I summoned the courage to defend climate science from those who misrepresent it I suffered harsh consequences. And so I mostly stood by and did next to nothing as my fellow environmentalists terrified the public." [xxv]

He is far from alone as the numerous quotations from very qualified climate scientists throughout this book clearly show. Yet many people today still believe the myth that all climate scientists are 100% behind climate change. This is totally wrong. If the list of above mentioned eco-scares shows us anything, it's that critical thinking needs to be applied whenever we read of any impeding environmental disaster. And that most certainly includes climate change.

4. The antihuman agenda

"Radical environmentalists have seized upon global warming as an excuse to justify their war on people to promote abortion and sterilization around the world."

Steven W. Mosher PhD, social scientist, author and president of the Population Research Institute

You don't have to listen to most secular environmentalists for too long to realize they have an antihuman agenda. The general attitude among them is; all forms of nature need to be preserved and protected at any cost, except human life.

"We humans are the greatest of earth's parasites."

Martin Henry Fischer, American physician and author

Most consider mankind to be the cause of all real and imaginary ecological problems. And in some cases this is true. Mankind has and does cause a lot of damage to nature including a substantial amount of environmental pollution that could be avoided. However, the radical environmentalist's solution is not the answer. Many of them want to reduce the number of people in the world in order to save Mother Earth.

"Instead of controlling the environment for the benefit of the population, perhaps we should control the population to ensure the survival of our environment."

Sir David Attenborough, naturalist and prolific wildlife documentary narrator

The Bible clearly teaches us the opposite is true. While creation does indeed declare the glory of God, Jesus clearly demonstrated that people are of far greater value to God than animals. In Mark 12: 11-12 we read the account of Jesus healing a man on the Sabbath, (and angering the Pharisees at the same time). Comparing a person rescuing a sheep, He clearly states, *"If you had a sheep that fell into a well on the Sabbath, wouldn't you work to pull it out? Of course you would. And how much more valuable is a person than a sheep!"*

In contrast to what secular environmentalists teach, human beings are not just another type of advanced animal. We are created in the image of God who regards mankind above all animals and all of creation. We are of great value to Him as is clearly stated in the book of James.

"He never changes or casts a shifting shadow. He chose to give birth to us by giving us his true Word. <u>And we, out of all creation, became his prized possession.</u>"
James 1:17b-18 NLT

The agenda to reduce the global population

Satan has a plan for mankind. And he finds people who agree with his program and then uses them. Jesus laid out the devil's agenda very clearly.

"The thief (satan) comes only to kill, steal and destroy."
John 10:10 NIV

The ungodly view that the global human population is too high and needs to be reduced in order to save "Mother Earth" is a major belief among environmentalists, secular politicians, and many of the climate change protesting masses.

"Third world nation's are producing too many children too fast ...it is time to ignore the controversy over family planning and cut out-of-control population growth."

Al Gore, former US Democratic presidential candidate and ardent climate change alarmist

Incidentally Al Gore, who has four children, suggests Africans should have fewer children because of climate change. This elitist antihuman belief is nothing new. Back in the early 1800s Thomas Malthus, a prominent secular English demographer and political economist, warned that the increasing global human population would eventually lead to mass starvation. His solution was forced sterilization. He even ENCOURAGED diseases like the bubonic plague in order to kill millions of economically poor people, and reduce the world's population.

"Instead of recommending cleanliness to the poor, we should encourage contrary habits. In our towns we should make the streets narrower, crowd more people into houses, and court the return of the (bubonic) plague."

Thomas Malthus, pessimist English demographer and political economist, early 1800s

Of course Thomas Malthus, just like most who suggest such terrible "remedies" today, didn't see themselves or any of their own family or friends as part of the problem. They have a fascination with killing off poorer members of society.

This is a view shared by nearly all who advocate for population control.

In a similar vein, Margaret Sanger, the racist and eugenicist founder of abortion group Planned Parenthood, believed the same things. Her solution was to promote abortion in order to kill as many babies as possible, especially those of African American, Jewish and Slavic ethnic origins, as well as those with disabilities who she referred to as "human weeds" and "reckless breeders". [xxvi]

"It was a great privilege when I was told that I would receive this award. I admire Margaret Sanger enormously. Her courage, her tenacity, her vision ... When I think about what she did all those years ago in Brooklyn, taking on archetypes, taking on attitudes and accusations flowing from all directions, I'm really in awe of her. There are a lot of lessons we can learn from her life, from the causes she launched and fought for and scarified for so greatly."

Hilary Clinton, upon accepting the Planned Parenthood Margaret Sanger award, 2014[xxvii], [xxviii]

Today many in leftist political circles laud and honor Margaret Sanger as a great person and someone they "admire". Somehow they totally ignore the fact that Margaret Sanger not only admired Hitler and approved of his ideas, but she also spoke before Klu Klux Klan meetings. Her true views are on full display in her writings. She freely wrote and spoke of "eliminating minorities, the sick and the disabled through sterilization and segregation". Today her sick legacy lives on through the murderous organization she founded[17].

---

[17] If you are shocked by the background information on Planned Parenthood founder, Margaret Sanger, I encourage you to follow the links and explore this information for yourself.

Green washed socialist cultural elites

The same thinking that drives the abortion industry is rampant at the United Nations and in many national government circles. In order to cover up their true aims, politicians and bureaucrats use ambiguous terminology for their evil programs. Terms such as "human population planning", "depopulation" and "sustainable population advocacy" are used to put a gloss over the fact that they actually mean intentionally killing people to reduce the human population.

Harvard professor John Holdren is an example of a modern government bureaucrat just like Thomas Malthus and Margaret Sanger before him. Holdren served as one of President Clinton's science advisors and was senior advisor to President Barack Obama on science and technology issues and policy.

Holdren, in his own words is obsessed with "global overpopulation". He was and is in favor of a host of barbaric measures to "regulate" population growth. Some of these measures include: compulsory abortion, long-term sterilization capsules to be implanted in people (only to be removed with "official permission"), compulsory sterilization of women after the birth of their first child. Furthermore, he advocated implementing the "Planetary Regime", a term he uses for a one-world global government with control and final say over what the world's optimum population should be for each country.[xxix] This evil Orwellian vision, in his own words, would serve to "restore a high-quality environment in North America" and to "de-develop" the United States and redistribute wealth among the nations.

Another example is Dr. Jeffery Sachs, director of the Earth Institute at Columbia University and an adviser to numerous United Nations committees. Dr. Sachs expresses concerns about "sustainable development" and global overpopulation. He uses the exact same arguments that Thomas Malthus used back in the 1800s. He warns that unless we reduce the number of people on the planet, our future looks "grim" and we will face environmental catastrophe. While his concerns may sound noble, his solution reveals his true motivation. Like many academics, Dr. Sachs promotes the fantasy that the world can simply abandon cheap and abundant fossil fuels, and transition to unreliable and expensive alternative "renewable" energy production, without destroying the world's economy in the process. At the same time, he believes poorer countries need to reduce their populations via any means possible.[xxx]

John Holdren and Dr. Jeffery Sachs are typical of the green washed socialist cultural elites embedded throughout academia and liberal governments around the globe. They are far from alone. There are hundreds of influential individuals in positions of authority in academia, governments and in global bodies such as the United Nations and similar organizations. Their desire is to control other people, and will use any means they deem necessary to bring about the green utopia they envision. They are not concerned about the fact that a few hundred million people or more might be killed along the way, as long as it's not their family or friends.

Voluntary Human Extinction

Even more extreme are groups like the Voluntary Human Extinction Movement. They go out of their way to encourage people to kill themselves or not have children in order to save the environment.[xxxi] Their stated mission is *"Phasing out the human race by voluntarily ceasing to breed will allow earth's biosphere to return to good health."*

Not surprisingly they twist scriptures to claim that when God told Adam and Eve to be fruitful and multiple, they say it refers to *"God is instructing us to reforest, re-establish wildlife habitat, enable wildlife to flourish, and replenish earth with His blessed creatures."* [18]

---

[18] http://vhemt.org/philrel.htm#religions

5. The misguided church

"What good is it that the Son of God was born 2000 years ago ... when for our own short-term financial gain we sell off our children's future and smugly watch our planet burn?"

Dr. Rod Bower, Anglican Priest[xxxii]

Incredible as it may seem many traditional church denominations and Christians are on the wrong side of the climate change debate. This is one of my main motivations in taking the time to research and write this book. There are too many followers of Christ who have failed to discern the truth! They have veered off course, believing we need to save planet earth, having been taken in by the environmentalist's myth of climate change. Many use the exact same talking points as the UN IPCC (Intergovernmental Panel Climate Change) and radical climate alarmist groups. They fail to understand that the focus of the church is always on saving people, not the planet. Jesus said in Matthew 6:21 *" Where your treasure is, there your heart will be as well."* Where we focus our attention, is what we will worship.

Some Christian leaders use the argument of "stewardship" to justify their support for the theory of man-made climate change. They make statements such as, *"We need to be good stewards of the earth and preserve it because the Lord made it."* They fail to understand that stewardship doesn't mean creation first, people second.

Confused believers have even joined forces with extreme environmental group, Extinction Rebellion, which boasts its own "Christian wing". They claim they are *"following in the footsteps of Jesus"* as they plan protests, block roads and disrupt the lives of ordinary citizens.[xxxiii]

Below are some examples of statements made by different mainline Christian denominations that believe the church should support climate change action:

From the official Church of England website, *"We believe that responding to climate change is an essential part of our responsibility to safeguard God's creation. Our environmental campaign exists to enable the whole church to address - in faith, practice and mission - the issue of climate change."* [xxxiv]

United Methodist Church statement on climate change:

"The crisis facing God's earth is clear. We, as stewards, have failed to live into our responsibility to care for creation and have instead abused it in ways that now threaten life around the planet. The scientific consensus is clear that human activities are leading to a warming of the surface temperatures of the planet and the effects of this warming are being felt now and will be felt more intensely in years to come.

As a matter of stewardship and justice, Christians must take action now to reduce global warming pollution and stand in solidarity with our brothers and sisters around the world whose land, livelihood and lives are threatened by the global climate crisis." [xxxv]

In 2019 the United Methodist church even tried to pass a motion to make it a "chargeable offense" for anyone to deny climate change from the pulpit.[xxxvi]

Likewise Pope Francis has on numerous occasions called for climate change action, and agrees with the UN IPCC declaring we have a "climate emergency". [xxxvii]

In Europe many national church groups such as the Danish National Council of Churches and in the United Kingdom, the Eco Church scheme have committed to support the climate change agenda.[xxxviii]

And in a bizarre display, students at Union Theological Seminary set up a display of plants to confess their "climate sins" to. Proud of their deed, they tweeted out:

"Today in chapel, we confessed to plants. Together, we held our grief, joy, regret, hope, guilt and sorrow in prayer, offering them to the beings who sustain us but whose gift we often fail to honor. What do you confess to the plants in your life?" [xxxix]

In a similar manner some churches have created written prayers of confession, absolution and intercession for believers to use in "confessing and repenting of their climate change and environmental sins", and asking God to forgive them for "abusing" His creation. [xl]

Any church promoting these kinds of prayers or confessions has totally misunderstood the Gospel. The mission of the church is to take the good news of Jesus to the world. Only the very deceived could believe that the church should be focused more on preserving the planet, than reaching the lost and making disciples of all men! The Lord Jesus Christ didn't step down from eternity to save nature. His sole purpose was to make a way for fallen sinful mankind to be able to get back into their rightful relationship with God the Father. Any church, pastor or Christian who preaches or teaches otherwise is confused and potentially entering into teaching heresy. Allowing climate change or concern for the environment to hi-jack the pulpit is a strategy of the anti-Christ spirit and should never be tolerated.

Just like the churches in the book of Revelation, those involved need to repent and return to their first love.

6. Marketing climate change

In order to gain broad public support for the concept of man-made climate change, a credible story line had to be manufactured, and sold in a way to achieve acceptance. In this chapter we will look at the main players who have concocted the "climate change" narrative and how it has been "sold" to the world.

Climate change branding

Firstly, in order to market and sell anything, you need a catchy name. So how did we end up with "climate change"? The term "climate change" is simply the latest in an ever-changing list of names that have been upgraded over the years. This is not because the science changed, but because branding is super important if you are going to sell a big concept to the world. And great branding begins with a good, easy to remember name. Something like "unusual climate events" or "strange weather phenomena" just doesn't cut it.

Many people assume climate change is a fairly recent concept. However, what the climate cult currently calls "climate change" began over fifty years ago. Back in the

1970s it was labeled "inadvertent climate modification", and with a brand name like that, no one paid much attention.

Next up was "the greenhouse effect" which gained some public attention but not enough. So "global warming" was invented and that did well for many years. However, global warming as a brand had some major deficiencies. For a start, it could only be applied to warm weather events. And that was okay for a while. However, just as the global warming story started to get some traction, the slight warming of the last century stopped around 1997. And there has been no warming from then until the present time. So that was clearly a problem for the use of the term "global warming"!

And the winning brand is …

Activist scientists understood that in order to continue to gain acceptance the branding name "global warming" simply had to go. One of the inventive names that was tried out was "global weirding" (claiming the world's weather is "weird"). And even "global melting" which was maybe slightly dramatic as the climate was no longer heating up. In the end, around 2013, "climate change" was crowned the winner as it allowed the inclusion of cold weather events.

Now ALL kinds of weather events could be claimed to be caused by "climate change". Even snow out of season could now be blamed on mankind's activities. Senator Barbara Boxer was one of the first to use the "snow-is-climate-change-too" card in May 2013:

"Yeah it's going to get hot, but you're also going to have snow in the summer in some places."

In the past that was simply late snowfall (if it occurred early in summer) or early snowfall (late in summer), but now it was "climate change".

Today, it doesn't matter what the weather is doing, everything is blamed on "climate change". Naturally occurring wildfires, too much rain, too little rain, hot weather, cold weather, anything goes. Even events that are not even remotely connected to weather at all are now regularly blamed on climate change. It's all marketing and most of the world has bought it.

The truth about the UN IPCC

Any discussion about the promotion of climate change has to start with the biggest player behind the global promotion of climate alarmism. And that is the UN IPCC (United Nations Intergovernmental Panel on Climate Change). This is the organization responsible for many of the outrageous apocalyptic pronouncements we hear politicians, celebrities and the media making about the "climate emergency". So who and what are they?

The UN IPCC is first and foremost a political organization made up of representatives of national governments from around the globe. The truth however is the UN IPCC is also staffed with hundreds of environmental radicals. These are drawn from NGOs and government bureaucrats who add their propaganda message to all outgoing communications.

This intergovernmental body portrays itself as the authoritative scientific organization on global climate change issues. And yes there certainly are well-qualified scientists working for and advising the IPCC. However, as has been pointed out numerous times by equally qualified scientists, the whole decision making process behind the UN IPCC has been corrupted by huge amounts of political, financial and ideological pressure. Public relations bureaucrats edit every document they release to ensure nothing deviates from the official IPCC interpretation of the facts.

In George Orwell's famous dystopian novel, "1984" the "Ministry of Truth" determined what the population should believe. Any facts that didn't line up with the official version were erased via memory holes, the deletion of all records and altering of data. These "thought police" were ever-present to punish anyone who dared to disagree with the carefully crafted official government propaganda version of events.

The UN IPCC today has more in common with the George Orwell's Ministry of Truth than most people realize. They are not the unbiased arbitrators of truth they pretend to be. Even worse, the majority of the world's mass media and educational systems unwittingly act as mouthpieces disseminating their official propaganda on climate change.

"The IPCC has become too political. Many scientists have not been able to resist the siren call of fame, research funding and meetings in exotic places that awaits them if they are willing to compromise scientific principles and integrity in support of the man-made global warming doctrine."

Professor Johannes Oerlemans, Dutch climatologist, University of Utrecht

Dr Aynsley Kellow, another scientist who worked on the UN IPCC reports, bluntly states: [xli]

"I'm not holding my breath for criticism to be taken on board, which underscores a fault in the whole peer review process for the IPCC. There is no chance of a chapter [of the IPCC report] ever being rejected for publication, no matter how flawed it might be."

Many climate scientists disagree with the UN IPCC

In an attempt to avoid debate, many climate alarmists claim, "the science is settled" on climate change. Yet there are many climate scientists and those in closely aligned fields, who have worked on the underlying climate research used by the UN IPCC and do not agree with the way climate change is presented. Some of these scientists were formally part of the UN IPCC and now openly criticize the so-called "gold standard" IPCC reports. [xlii], [xliii] The media and many politicians by and large are either ignorant of this fact or ignore it.

"This is the biggest scientific fraud ever perpetrated on the family of man. I'm really appalled at how the scientific community has sold out for big research grants and to get their name highlighted in the faculty journal and get invited to U.N. conferences." [xliv]

Steven W. Mosher, social scientist, author and president of the Population Research Institute

For a scientist, agreeing with what the global governing body wants, will secure their financial future. However, disagreement gets scientists labeled as "climate deniers" who are liable to lose huge $ in research funding, and possibly even being blacklisted by many universities. And big money is at stake. Estimates vary from hundreds of $billions to over several $trillion dollars in climate change research, project funding, government sponsored programs, all being given out to those who agree with the UN IPCC account of man-made climate change. Despite this lure of money, many top scientists have walked away from supporting the UN IPCC and its climate alarmism claims.

"I have become increasingly concerned about the integrity of climate research, which is being compromised by the politicization of the science."

"These dynamics are not operating in a manner that is healthy for either the science or the policy process."

Dr. Judith Curry, formally of Georgia Institute of Technology and a 30-year climate science veteran, in a statement testifying before a United States Senate panel on climate change. [xlv]

Dissenting climate scientists have claimed repeatedly that the UN IPCC reports are not only full of errors, but have totally ignored contrary evidence, way overblown any perceived risks and manipulated models to support their theories. [xlvi]

"The [IPCC] climate change statement is an orchestrated litany of lies."

Dr. Vincent Gray, a former IPCC expert reviewer for over 18 years, who resigned from the Royal Society of New Zealand to protest the inaccuracies in the UN IPCC report on climate change [xlvii]

"The UN IPCC have truly sunk to a level of hilarious incoherence."

"They (UN IPCC) are proclaiming increased confidence in their models as the discrepancies between their models and observations increase." [xlviii]

Meteorology Professor Richard Lindzen, Massachusetts Institute of Technology who has published hundreds of

scientific reports including being the lead author on the third
UN IPCC climate change report

Climate experts Patrick Michaels and Paul Knappenberger with the Center for the Study of Science at the Cato Institute Think Tank in Washington DC have accused the UN IPCC of producing "misleading reports" that are "entirely self-serving" and furthermore, are "completely useless as a basis to form opinions (or policy) related to human energy choices and their influence on the climate."[xlix]

Professor Judith Curry, former chair of the School of Earth and Atmospheric Sciences at the Georgia Institute of Technology is another highly esteemed climate scientist who disagrees with most of the UN IPCC conclusions, as reported in her respected climate blog, "Climate etc.". In a 2013 article she wrote for the Financial Post calling for the UN IPCC to be killed off after spending $billions over decades without offering any proof that mankind has caused global warming. Yet here we are another 7 years later, still with no proof, still more $billions wasted yet the UN IPCC is even louder than ever.

Scientific organizations that disagree with climate change alarmism

And in addition to thousands of climate scientists disagreeing with the UN IPCC, there are a growing number of climate change and climate policy scientific groups and independent foundations that oppose the myth of a "climate emergency". A few of these are listed below:

Climate Intelligence (CLINTEL) founded by Emeritus Professor of Geophysics, Guus Berkhout and science journalist Marcel Crok in the Netherlands. Nearly 1,000 scientists from around the world, including Nobel Laureates have signed their World Climate Declaration stating that there is no climate emergency. The most up-to-date version of both the Declaration and the list of signatories can be found on www.clintel.org

The CO₂ Coalition is a scientific policy group that was established to educate thought leaders, policy makers and the public on the positive benefits of increased carbon dioxide. The CO₂ Coalition consists of leading climate scientists and energy economists who stand against the misinformation that increased carbon dioxide is a danger to our planet. Well-funded climate alarmists are engaged in a campaign to censor their views on Facebook and other social media platforms. https://co2coalition.org

Nongovernmental International Panel on Climate Change (NIPCC) is an international panel of nongovernment scientists and scholars who have come together to present a comprehensive, authoritative, and realistic assessment of the science and economics of global warming. Because it is not a government agency, and because its members are not predisposed to believe climate change is caused by human greenhouse gas emissions, NIPCC is able to offer an independent "second opinion" of the evidence reviewed – or not reviewed – by the Intergovernmental Panel on Climate Change (IPCC) on the issue of global warming. http://climatechangereconsidered.org

The Global Warming Policy Foundation, calls for "common sense on climate change" and is mostly opposed to UN IPCC climate change findings. Many of its members formally worked for the UN IPCC. http://www.thegwpf.org

Environmental nonprofits

The list of environmentalist nonprofits openly committed to supporting climate change is very long indeed. Even larger is the untold number of activist supporters and social justice warriors these groups call on and mobilize. There is hardly any sector of society that isn't being targeted by one or many of these environmental groups. Most are very political, making their presence felt in both state and national elections, with many openly committed to removing conservatives from office.

Here is a short list of some of the largest and loudest radical environmental groups. Between them they wield $billions in funding all directed towards their activist goals:

350.org
Alliance for Climate Education (ACE)
Audubon Society
Citizens Climate Lobby
Climate Adoption Mitigation E-Learning (CAMEL)
Climate Change Education Partnership (CCEP)
Climate Reality Project
Climate Solutions
ConservAmerica
Conservation International
Conservation Land Foundation
Greenpeace USA
Earth Justice
Environmental Defence Fund (EDF)
Environmental Justice Foundation (EJF)
Extinction Rebellion
I See Change
Land Trust Alliance
Moms Clean Air Force
Mothers Out Front

National Wildlife Federation (NWF)
Natural Resources Defense Council (NRDC)
Nature Conservancy
NexGen Climate
Polar Bear International
Rain Forest Action Network (RAN)
Sierra Club
Sunrise Movement
The Wilderness Society
Union of Concerned Scientists
World Wildlife Federation (WWF)

In addition to the nonprofits listed above, there are thousands of smaller, grassroots environmental groups and causes around the globe that raise money directly and receive funding from grants.

Foundations and Funds[19]

A lot of the really big money, many $billions, behind nearly all of the nonprofit groups mentioned above comes from both private and governmental foundations and sovereign wealth funds. Many are open about their support of climate change advocacy and research projects. Fewer speak of their funding climate change protests and marches. All are deeply committed to "tackling climate change". Most likewise are committed to promoting a secular new world order.

The following is a short list of some of the more prominent foundations, many funded by public figures,

---

[19] As a point of clarity, many of the same foundations are involved in sound, social improvement projects helping the poor and tackling injustice in some of the poorest nations and communities worldwide. Many do some good work.

companies and governmental programs that provide climate change promotional and activist funding:

Bezos Earth Fund *(Foundation of Amazon founder, Jeff Bezos)*
Bill & Melinda Gates Foundation (*Foundation of Microsoft co-founder Bill Gates and his wife, Melinda)*
Climate Foundation
ClimateWorks Foundation
Clinton Foundation *(Foundation of Bill and Hillary Clinton)*
European Climate Foundation
Ford Foundation *(Ford Motor Company founders family foundation)*
Global Greengrants Fund
Green Climate Fund
Hewlett Foundation *(Foundation of Hewlett Packard co-founder William Hewlett and his wife)*
Kresge Foundation *(Foundation of S.S. Kresge whose businesses became Sears and Kmart)*
MacArthur Foundation *(Family foundation of John D. MacArthur and his wife)*
Moore Charitable Foundation
Open Society Foundation *(Foundation of billionaire hedge fund manager, George Soros)*
PGA Family Foundation *(Foundation of Microsoft co-founder Paul Allen and his sister)*
The David and Lucile Packard Foundation *(Foundation of Hewlett Packard co-founder David Packard and his wife)*
The Leonardo DiCaprio Foundation
The Paulson Institute
The Pew Charitable Trust
The Rockefeller Foundation
Skoll Global Threats Fund
United Nations Foundation

Hollywood and the entertainment industry

Hollywood celebrities and entertainers have likewise long supported environmental causes. The promotion of and support of man-made climate change is almost universal in tinsel town and across the music industry. Leading the charge is a who's who of the celebrity world from almost every Hollywood actor promoting climate change. Musicians and bands of every kind likewise use their platforms to promote and support climate change advocacy among their fans. Together celebrities and entertainers influence millions of people to support and follow their lead.

The Media

"The news media have been making apocalyptic pronouncements about climate change since the late 1980s, and do not seem disposed to stop."

Michael Shellenberger, Time Magazine "Hero of the Environment," president of Environmental Progress

The majority of the world's media almost universally believes in and supports the idea of man-made climate change. No matter what evidence is presented, no matter how many scientists come out against climate change, the media are so invested in the narrative that they helped create, they cannot change track.

Most newspapers and cable TV news channels today are more like fictional drama or even political propaganda outlets. Reporters and cable hosts have shown their true colors. Their reports are often ideologically driven. They present their biased viewpoints and pretend they are objective reporters. They cherry pick stories that match their own mostly left leaning political and ideological agendas,[20] and totally ignore others that should be reported [1]. They speculate without checking for accuracy, and overblow stories and dramatize them in order to get clicks and views. Ratings and viewers matter more to media outlets than anything else. Maybe it was always this way, but today with so many channels to exploit, we are all exposed to more media than ever.

When it comes to reporting on environmental issues, the media are responsible for a large part of the hysteria and irrational fear that climate change alarmism has produced in many people. Consider the following exaggerated headlines, each specially written as dramatically as possible:

The Point of No Return: Climate Change Nightmares Are Already Here, Rolling Stone magazine, August 5, 2015

Should we be having kids in the age of Climate Change? NPR, August 18, 2016

A new report on climate change predicts a bleak future, News Version, October 8, 2018

AOC (Alexandria Ocasio-Cortez) says she is awakened at 3.30 AM scared because of climate change, PJ Media, August 29, 2019

Flooded future: Global vulnerability to sea level rise worse than previously understood, Climate Central.org, October 29, 2019

---

[20] Arizona State University and Texas A&M University 2018 study found the ratio of journalists at major news outlets was 13 self proclaimed media "liberals" to every one "conservative".

89

In bleak report, U.N. says drastic action is only way to avoid worst effects of climate change, The Washington Post, November 26, 2019

These are just a small example of the over-the-top, "we-are-all-doomed" scaremongering indoctrination that goes on 24/7/365 via every possible channel. No wonder, so many people are confused and filled with a fear of the future.

7. Indoctrinating youth

"But whoever causes one of these little ones who believe in Me to sin, it would be better for him if a millstone were hung around his neck, and he were drowned in the depth of the sea."
The words of Jesus, Matthew 18:6

Removing the Bible from schools

The Bible is the standard of truth upon which the worldview of every born-again Christian stands. Because of a Supreme Court decision in 1962 prayer was banned in school assemblies. This then led to the removal of Bibles from schools in 1963. With this standard of truth taken away, all kinds of deceptive lies have been introduced into the education system. The results are clear for everyone to see. Academic achievements, including SAT scores plummeted, juvenile crime and drug use increased, school behavior deteriorated and out-of-wedlock births shot up.

Schools today indoctrinate children with secular teaching in almost every area of study. And the majority of the church does very little about it. It's way past time for Christians to get involved and take back the educational system in which their children are being raised.[21] (Please pause and read the footnote below)

The result of secular academic teaching

Today the majority of the world's youth and young adults are convinced that civilization will end unless urgent climate change action is taken.[li] This is what decades of secular academic brainwashing has produced. Education is so valued in our society that many parents never question what or who is teaching their children. Deliberately targeted environmental scare tactics have taught almost everyone under the age of 40 that humans, and in particular adults, are killing the planet. This is so ingrained in the minds of most millennials and younger generations, that climate change is now considered the top issue among younger voters in nearly every election. [lii]

A generation of zealots

Children are exploited and used as pawns to further the globalist climate change agenda. The ongoing scare tactics of climate cult activists are central to creating extreme anxiety among school age children, teenagers and young adults. This is then amplified by most of what they see online, in social media and hear in classrooms. UNESCO (United Nations Educational, Scientific and Cultural Organization) has made climate change education one of its key objectives.

---

[21] If there is one point you get from this book, it is that too many children have been led astray by secular curriculum and teachers. This is abundantly clear when you look at young people who have gone off to collage, only to lose their faith.

"Education is an essential element of the global response to climate change. It helps young people understand and address the impact of global warming, encourages changes in their attitudes and behavior and helps them adapt to climate change-related trends."

UNESCO website statement [liii]

UNESCO understands that targeting children with their message will create an army of future radicals.[liv] They know politicians are vulnerable to the impassioned plea of children asking for help. And they use this to their advantage in promoting the climate change agenda, stoking fear and panic along the way.

Teenage climate activist Greta Thunberg is a prime example. She started on her journey to climate zealot at age 7 when she was taught about global pollution and climate change in school. In the words of her father,[lv] Greta "underwent trauma and depression", stopped eating and only talked to close family members. At the same time she was diagnosed with Asperger Syndrome, obsessive-compulsive disorder and selective mutism.

Her parents claim that by talking about climate change, it helps cure her condition. They apparently don't see a problem with using a vulnerable teenager to promote their radical worldview. Her scripted "performances" at high profile media events have since made her a celebrity and granted her an audience with the UN, global monarchs, Hollywood actors and even with Pope Francis.[lvi]

The media management and grooming of Greta is worthy of any A-Rated movie actor or politician. In interviews she purposely provides professionally written sound bytes so the media can quote her. Typical examples being *"climate change is an existential threat to the planet"*, " *we are facing the biggest crisis humanity has ever faced"* and *"we must try and save what we can save."*

Student protests

With encouragement from activist groups, large crowds (with claims of up to 6 million people) of mostly students and youth have participated in so-called climate action global protests.[lvii] Since 2019 and prior to the current coronavirus outbreak, the movement had spread to almost every country around the world. Skipping school to protest has become a standard part of life for many school age climate change believers. Slogans such as *"I'll be at school when the world is cool"*, *"If you don't act like adults, we will"*, and *"Planet over profit"*, reflect the radicalized thinking of the protesters.

In the classroom

A large influencing factor behind the radicalization of many students and young adults today has come from college and university professors, holding strong left leaning political and social views. Many are self-proclaimed socialists and Marxists. This is borne out not only by their bias when teaching, but backed up by studies looking at faculty voter registration records. These show liberal professors outnumbered their conservative colleagues by a ratio of 12 to 1.[lviii] This is largest gap between the two in any profession.[lix] And the gap is continuing to widen with an increasing number of liberal academics taking jobs across almost all teaching subjects.[lx] This self-reinforcing trend is driven by the fact that liberal minded individuals are drawn to careers in academia, as they perceive that most academics hold liberal views. So either consciously or unconsciously, schools and universities have created an entire system of anti-conservative thought. This is ripe for the promotion of left leaning views on subjects like climate change, the environment, abortion, gender and other social topics.

This worldview was exemplified in June 2019 when 7,000 colleges and universities from around the world declared a "climate emergency", along with a plan detailing how they intend to address it. [lxi] Their suggestions include going "carbon neutral", mobilizing more resources for climate change research, and creating even more climate change curricula to mold young minds. This was detailed in the following common declaration:

> "The young minds that are shaped by our institutions must be equipped with the knowledge, skills, and capability to respond to the ever-growing challenges of climate change," "We all need to work together to nurture a habitable planet for future generations and to play our part in building a greener and cleaner future for all."

With an increase in climate change radicalism among students and faculty alike, it's not surprising that campuses across the country are seeing an explosion in the number of more conservative minded speakers being disinvited from speaking at events.

Censorship of student free speech is likewise under fire. It's not unusual to hear of conservative students being targeted by teachers and professors for their personal views, including those concerning climate change.[22] If there is one thing highly educated academic leftists hate, it's for anyone to disagree with their worldview. Such is the religious fervor with which climate change beliefs are held. Some even use

---

[22] Of course this works both ways. However, there are many more cases of conservative lecturers being targeted by liberal leaning students than the other way round.

their positions of power to bully and discriminate against those they deem "climate deniers" among both students and other faculty members.[lxii]

Social media

The online virtual world of social media plays a huge part in shaping youth culture. The problem is social media has become a cesspool of misinformation that deceives many people, both young and old alike.

At the time of writing, teenager climate change activist Greta Thunberg has nearly 9 million Instagram followers and millions of views and likes across other platforms. Hundreds of lesser-known youth activists likewise fill every national and international social media site with blogs, posts, videos and comments. They promote the global climate change agenda and exploit the teenage need for significance and inclusion. Teenagers are more influenced by peer-pressure than any other age group. They will go to extreme lengths to fit in. We can understand that when most of their peer group and idols follow a trend or support a cause, there is tremendous pressure to "fit in" and do the same.

Additionally social media companies use their platforms to enforce their worldview of social issues on everyone else. Twitter, YouTube and Google have long engaged in censorship of conservative personalities and content they don't agree with. [lxiii, lxiv] Likewise Facebook and its army of hyper partisan fact checkers are always ready to "fact check" and mark as "false" and even outright block posts that don't line up with their mostly progressive, leftist views.

An example is of Dr. Patrick Michaels, formally the president of the association of state climatologists and an expert reviewer and former author for the UN's climate change panel. In his very qualified opinion, he stated that approximately half of the 1°C/1.8°F increase in global temperature in the later half of last century was natural, and the other half was in his opinion due to human activity. Facebook fact checkers disagreed with him and marked his post as "false"! [lxv]

This intolerant trend is only likely to continue, giving everyone, especially young people a very one-sided view of important social issues.

8. The climate change end game

"One has to free oneself from the illusion that international climate policy is environmental policy. This has almost nothing to do with the environmental policy anymore, with problems such as deforestation or the ozone hole. We will redistribute de facto the world's wealth by climate policy."

Dr. Ottmar Edenhoefer, co-chair of the UN IPCC working group on Mitigation of Climate Change[23]

In order to get elected and stay in power, most modern politicians will say almost anything; often making promises without any regard for the truth. They are like modern versions of Pontius Pilate, the governor of the Roman province of Judaea when he presided over the trial of Jesus. When faced with truth, Pilate simply denied it and walked away giving the crowds what they wanted rather than making a stand for what he knew was correct.

---

[23] Dr. Edenhoefer is also the chief economist of the Potsdam Institute for Climate Impact Research in Germany. One of the climate centers helping to write climate policy for the EU, the UN, and the World Bank.

Jesus answered, "the reason I was born and came into the world is to testify to the truth. Everyone on the side of truth listens to me."

"What is truth?" retorted Pilate.
John 18:37b – 38 NIV

We see the same immoral attitude in many leaders and journalists today. It's not that they don't know truth, it's rather their moral compasses have been so corrupted they have no regard for the truth.

Tim Wirth, former U.S. Undersecretary of State for Global Affairs and the person most responsible for setting up the Kyoto Protocol [24], didn't try to hide that he and those in the Clinton US administration at the time were using climate change as a front for their ultimate agenda:

"We've got to ride the global warming issue. Even if the theory of global warming is wrong, we will be doing the right thing in terms of economic policy and environmental policy."

Tim Wirth, former U.S. Undersecretary of State for Global
Affairs

This is why politicians love a crisis or disaster, because every crisis or disaster is a chance for them to implement their solution to the problem. Thus the politicizing of the environment should come as no surprise. Climate change and environmental disasters, real or imagined, are no different to them. They are a means to an end for politicians to gain more power. In the case of climate change that power is mostly in

---

[24] The Kyoto Protocol was an international treaty committing countries to reduce carbon emissions as part of the UN climate change strategy.

the form of increased regulations, higher taxes or taking away control and resources from individuals in order to "save" the environment, the oceans, the forests, the animals or the planet.

In the 2020 election cycle, climate change is being used as a tool of far-left politicians to promote their policies. *Climate Power 2020* is an example of what the country can expect when a leftist leader is next elected. An organization led by Stacey Abrams, John Kerry and a host of far-left leaning political activists, are calling for an end to all fossil fuels and the censorship and intimidation of any who oppose them. And in a move more expected in a Communist dictatorship than in the land of the free, in an open letter to Facebook, they "demand" that any climate views they don't agree with are "taken down". [lxvi]

Socialism is the real agenda

"The goal of socialism is communism."

Vladimir Lenin, Russian revolutionary and responsible for more deaths than Adolf Hitler

"Climate change is caused by capitalism, and merely attempting to reform capitalism will not stop global warming; it is impossible to work within the existing system if we want to save the planet. We must replace it with a new social and economic system entirely." [lxvii]

"People's Climate Rally" speaker, California, 2014

Many have long written and warned of the "red center" of the environmental movement. As the Soviet Union was collapsing, Mikhail Gorbachev, then secretary general of the Communist Party, called for the establishment of an international environmental monitoring system. This was seen by many as part of the ongoing Soviet attempt to infiltrate global institutions.

In a similar fashion, most of the UN sponsored environmental programs have the full support of every socialist and communist government. Most calling for more centralized U.N. control. The result is a weakening of national sovereignty. This is a key part of the globalist socialist and Marxist agenda. So it's no surprise to witness the writers and the promoters of the "New Green Deal" using climate alarmism. This is fundamental to promoting increased centralized government control, and ultimately socialism upon the American people.

The Green New Deal

" Climate change is here + we've got a deadline: 12 years left to cut emissions in half. A #GreenNewDeal is our plan for a world and future worth fighting for."

Alexandria Ocasio-Cortez, US Representative (Bronx & Queens, NY) via Twitter, April 17, 2019

Radical environmental group, the Sunrise Movement, originally wrote the report before it was introduced to the American public by Democrat Socialist, Rep. Alexandria Ocasio-Cortez. The Green New Deal is really nothing more than an attempt to harness the scare of climate change. The objective would be big government taking over the energy and travel sectors along with the food and farming industries. And to redistribute wealth, all in an attempt to remake society as a centrally governed socialist utopia.

It's estimated that the Green New Deal proposal will cost up to $93 trillion in new government spending over ten years.

Basically this is money the government doesn't have! This didn't stop almost every 2020 Democratic US Presidential candidate from announcing his or her support for the proposal.[25]

The architects behind the "Green New Deal" have even admitted as much, that their aim is not really even about the environment, it's about installing a centralized socialist government to run the economy.

"The interesting thing about the Green New Deal is it wasn't originally a climate thing at all," Saikat Chakrabarti, Rep. Alexandria Ocasio-Cortez's chief of staff confessed according to the Washington Post. *"Do you guys think of it as a climate thing?"* Chakrabarti then asked. *"Because we really think of it as a how-do-you-change-the-entire-economy thing."* [lxviii]

Of course that isn't what Ocasio-Cortez claimed when she introduced her proposal or in any subsequent statements.

While calling for a "detailed national, industrial and economic mobilization plan" to make the US economy "greenhouse gas emissions neutral", the Green New Deal contains a re-hash of everything extreme liberals have ever wanted. All tied up in a new package with a new marketing name: "Green NEW Deal".

Why would they even think they can get away with this? The answer is part of the problem in America today. Many voters simply no longer care about the "details", as long as the "headline" or sound bite resonates with them. Politicians know this. And have adapted their speeches to include

---

[25] A January 2019 Pew survey showed 67% of Democrats in Congress said dealing with climate change should be a top priority versus 21% of Republicans. And no Republicans supported the Green New Deal.

numerous crowd-pleasing sound bites that are slim on specifics. Promising voters what they can't deliver seems to work.

The financial burden

An example is Senator Bernie Sanders releasing a $16.3 trillion megaproposal to support the Green New Deal.[lxix] No sane economist supports this and dozens have said so. Even many from the left side of the political spectrum didn't agree with his math. The US economy couldn't afford it. If for example, the federal government spent 100% of tax revenues on his plan, (abandoning all spending on the military, education, healthcare and all social security programs), it still wouldn't cover the cost. However, in order to sell his ideas to the public, all Sanders had to do was promise the creation of "20 million new jobs, and to completely stop all carbon emissions by 2050". Both of which he could never deliver. There simply isn't enough money to pay for his schemes and still create new jobs.

This is how socialism works. Promise utopia and persuade the masses with empty pledges. And socialism once established nearly always morphs into full-blown Marxism. This ends with total government control and loss of personal freedoms. Of course by the time regular citizens figure it out they are stuck in a political system they can't get out of without a fight. Which is difficult to do when only the government has real weapons. This is what the citizens of Venezuela, Cuba, and other communist countries have discovered!

Enforcing compliance

"Fossil fuel executives should be criminally prosecuted for the destruction they have knowingly caused."

Bernie Sanders, former US Democratic party presidential candidate, Twitter, August 22, 2019

Going one-step further, in their quest to enforce change on humanity, many climate change advocates would like to hold climate inquisitions. Those deemed guilty of crimes against the planet could then be punished. This is nothing new. British born NASA chemist James Hansen originally started calling for oil firm CEOs to be put on trial back in 2008[lxx]. Additionally lawyers for the environment have been pushing for this for years, using the made-up term "ecocide[26]" (environmental genocide) as the charge. Now with climate change they have their opportunity.

Some such as democratic socialist Bernie Sanders are committed to charging those they deem to be "climate offenders" with "criminal charges". As quoted at the beginning of this section, his August 22, 2019 Twitter message reads:
"Fossil fuel executives should be criminally prosecuted for the destruction they have knowingly caused."

It's a pity that socialists don't apply the same standards to real socialist leaders who have killed, imprisoned, and

---

[26] Ecocide is now an official term, meaning "the destruction of large areas of the natural environment by such activity as nuclear warfare, over exploitation of resources, or the dumping of harmful chemicals". Many radical environmentalists expand this definition to include any activities they deem as harming Mother Nature.

impoverished millions with their policies. He also plans to sue the fossil fuel industry for billions of dollars to pay for his big socialist agenda. It should be noted that Mr. Sanders uses a car and flies on planes powered by the very products he wants to persecute other for producing. He even indicated he intends to fly more in private jets for his work.[lxxi] Just like other political and celebrity hypocrites, he feels its okay for him to use air travel, just not you and me.

He is not alone in his desire to punish business executives. Democratic lawmakers tried the same thing under the Obama administration. Arizona Democratic Rep. Raul Grijalva called for climate scientists who disagreed with climate change to be investigated using the RICO act (Racketeer Influenced and Corruption Organizations Act). Grijalva claimed these scientists and groups they worked with *"have knowingly deceived the American people about the risks of climate change, as a means to forestall America's response to climate change."*[lxxii]

Actress Jane Fonda feels the same way (and yes she also flies a lot and owns numerous huge energy guzzling properties). She wants "Nuremberg trials[27]" for not only energy industry executives but also for politicians who support them. And Bill Nye, the friendly TV, "science guy" feels the same. He has called for "climate change dissenters" to be jailed.[lxxiii] His comments sum up the secular climate cult's totalitarian views of "agree with us or we will persecute you and if necessary put you in jail" approach.

---

[27] The Nuremberg Trials were a series of trials that occurred in post-World War II Germany to provide a platform for justice against accused Nazi war criminals.

The end game

"A massive campaign must be launched to restore a high-quality environment in North America and to de-develop the United States. De-development means bringing our economic system (especially patterns of consumption) into line with the realities of ecology and the global resource situation. Redistribution of wealth both within and among nations is absolutely essential, if a decent life is to be provided for every human being."

John Holdren, science advisor to President Clinton and senior advisor on science and technology issues to President Barack Obama

Listen long enough to politicians and other leaders in the radical environmental movement, and their true agenda becomes very clear. While they believe in and support their earth-first environmental beliefs, most of their underlying drive is to usher in a mixture of hardcore Marxism and globalism. They clearly view the West and capitalism as evil and the cause of everything they oppose.

"We must now agree on a binding review mechanism under international law, so that this century can credibly be called a century of decarbonization."

German Chancellor Angela Merkel

The real underlying goals of politicians and globalists supporting the climate cult can be summarized as follows:

The redistribution of wealth among the nations. That is the forceful taking from the rich and giving to the poor. The UN's climate czar, Christina Figueres at the UN 2012 Climate Summit in Doha, Qatar was very clear about this:

"It must be understood that what is occurring here, ... is the whole climate change process is a complete transformation of the economic structure of the world."

Make no mistake; a large part of the climate change agenda is a power and wealth grab under the guise of science and environmental concerns.

Forceful population control by means of compulsory eugenics, compulsory sterilization, compulsory abortions and requiring government approval in order to have children.

The promotion and ultimately the introduction of a one-world government, under the auspices of the United Nations New World Order

Introduction of a one-world government

The United Nations New World Order Project is a grand scheme to advance "a new economic paradigm", "a new political order" and "a new world order for mankind". This is based on the UN's Global Goals for Sustainable Development" by 2030. The UN is not even trying to hide its ultimate agenda. It's all out in the open on its UN New World Order website. https://unnwo.org

Under the guise of saving the global economy and stopping climate change, the UN's Global Goals for Sustainable Development includes $30 trillion in funding towards achieving its 17 UN Global Goals. A larger part of this funding is for the promotion of climate change projects including:

"Affordable and clean energy", by which they mean "renewable energy". No cheap and abundant fossil fuels will be allowed. As I point out in a later chapter, the utopia of

108

"clean and cheap" renewable energy is a fantasy. Solar and wind powered energy is not reliable and it's not cheap compared to other solutions. Some early adopter nations in Europe have found this out to their detriment. And worst of all, so-called renewable energy is not as pollution free or good for the environment as it is claimed to be.

Solar panel manufacturing and recycling are a major source of environmental pollution. And wind powered turbines kill and maim millions of bats and birds annually. Many environmentalists freely admit this as the dead bird and bat carcasses pile up, killed by giant spinning wind turbine blades.

"Climate action". This is "taking urgent action to combat climate change and its impacts". These urgent actions include, adding more "climate change measures into policies and planning", "promoting mechanisms to raise capacity for planning and management" and several other equally nebulous grand sounding statements. All this actually does nothing to change the weather, save the planet or help people. Except of course it will help pay the committees, the consultants and the scientists who will all be funded by the $100 billion, the UN wants for this annually. In other words, this is another UN self-enrichment scam.

While several of the goals are written to sound like they will actually do good, such as "end all forms of malnutrition", "provide safe and affordable drinking water for all", etc. It's very clear from reading the finer details that massive control will have to be exerted at an international level, to achieve all the targets in each of the larger goals. UN globalists know this is not possible without a larger central government like the UN running everything including writing policies and policing outcomes. In other words, the UN New World Order is designed as a one-world government system where wealth will be redistributed among the nations. Children are to be indoctrinated with even more secular "sustainability development" ideology. Fossil fuels will be outlawed, and strict population reducing policies will be mandated. What is currently only seen in totalitarian society, where central governments control the means to production and consumption, the UN envisions these changes and policies for the whole world. This should be enough to wake up any freedom-loving individual! We must not be content to march down the road to the promised socialist paradise all in the name of saving the world from climate change.

Summary

This is an important topic because **the end result will most certainly cost us our freedom**. Ideas are slowly introduced into society until they gain acceptance. This is what is currently happening with the introduction of "friendly socialism" in the United States. Like many deceptions, socialism will cost more in the long run than most realize. It will cost us our religious freedoms, and inevitably destroy the economy.

Part 2: Debunking climate change myths

In Part 2 we will drill down on some of the claims associated with climate change and debunk the myths from the truth.

9. The truth about CO_2

Claim: We need to urgently reduce the amount of carbon dioxide in the atmosphere

"The most telling point is that after spending $30 billion on pure science research no one is able to point to a single piece of empirical evidence that man-made carbon dioxide has a significant effect on the global climate."

Joanne Nova, scientist and author, "Climate Money – the Climate Industry: $79 billion so far, trillions to come"

Carbon dioxide or CO_2, is a colorless, odorless trace gas that's naturally found within our atmosphere. There have been volumes of misinformation written about the "dangers" of CO_2. Yet it is important for all life on earth. Algae, cyanobacteria and plants use sunlight to convert CO_2 to oxygen. Far from being a "pollutant" as many climate alarmists call it, CO_2 is literally vital for all life on earth. And the increase in global CO_2 levels is actually doing much good, increasing crop yields and greening our planet. Trying to intentionally reduce CO_2 levels is totally counter productive to the needs of mankind and our environment.

Many scientists agree that the rise in CO_2 doesn't correlate very strongly with warming at all. Meteorology Professor Richard Lindzen from MIT (Massachusetts Institute of Technology), who served as the lead author on the third United Nations Intergovernmental Panel on Climate Change (UN IPCC) Report, and now one of the harshest critics of man-made climate change, had this to say regarding CO_2:

"What historians will definitely wonder about in future centuries is how deeply flawed logic, obscured by shrewd and unrelenting propaganda, actually enabled a coalition of powerful special interests to convince nearly everyone in the world that CO2 from human industry was a dangerous, planet-destroying toxin. <u>*It will be remembered as the greatest mass delusion in the history of the world – that CO2, the life of plants, was considered for a time to be a deadly poison"*</u>

Carbon dioxide is a very small component in our atmosphere

Listening to talk about our urgent need to "limit CO_2 production" most people are shocked to find out how little CO_2 there actually is in the earth's atmosphere. They assume it must be a large number, because the media talk about it so much whenever they promote the latest climate change disaster scenario.

The fact is CO_2 only makes up approximately 0.04% of the earth's atmosphere at 400 parts per million (400ppm). Yes! That's all! Carbon dioxide is such a small component of earth's atmosphere. To show CO_2 on a chart of the atmosphere gases, the line needs to be drawn at double its normal thickness just so it can be seen. (See image below)

The Gases that comprise Earth's Atmosphere

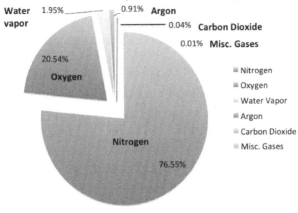

Water vapor 1.95%   0.91% Argon
        0.04% Carbon Dioxide
      0.01% Misc. Gases

20.54% Oxygen

- Nitrogen
- Oxygen
- Water Vapor
- Argon
- Carbon Dioxide
- Misc. Gases

Nitrogen

76.55%

CO_2 is just 0.04% of the Earth's atmosphere

So how much CO_2 does human activity contribute?

"During the last hundred years the temperature increased about 0.1 °C because of carbon dioxide. The human contribution was about 0.01 °C." [lxxiv]

Professors Jyrki Kauppinen (Physics) & P. Malmi, Finland, June 29, 2019

The vast majority of CO_2 in our atmosphere occurs naturally. CO_2 is found in all of earth's water sources including our oceans, rivers, lakes and underground water aquifers. The carbon cycle sees carbon flow naturally between earth's oceans, atmosphere, soil, living creatures and plants.

"My considered view is that we still know too little about the natural sources of global warming, despite the efforts of the United Nations IPCC (Intergovernmental Panel on Climate Change) to present it all as settled."

Pedro Schwartz, PhD, July 2020

And while human industrial activity does cause a net gain of some CO_2, most scientists agree human activity only contributes around 1% of the total each year. So to put that in perspective, out of all the CO_2 in our atmosphere, approximately 1% of it was caused by you and me. Let's repeat that. All the world's cars, planes and transportation and the output of the entire global industrial base and we only contribute 1% of the total CO_2 output. And this is really the number that climate alarmists have built their theory on when they talk about man-made climate change.

No correlation between temperature over the last century and the amount of CO_2 in the atmosphere

One of the biggest myths the climate alarmists repeat is the hypothesized link between increased atmospheric concentrations[28] of CO_2 and the tiny rise in global temperature last century. However, trying to tie the two together quickly starts to unravel when the edited computer models are taken away.[lxxv] According to the University of Alabama Huntsville's (UAH) climate science reporting, the temperature of the troposphere, (that is the lowest layer of the earth's atmosphere where most "weather" takes place), shows no increase at a time when carbon dioxide levels were increasing. They recorded the temperature of the lower atmosphere over the lower 48 states from 1978 to 2019 using satellite

---

[28] Levels of gases in the upper atmosphere are measured at x number of parts per million. It's claimed that there were 280 parts per million of CO_2 in the atmosphere before the industrial age began, and the fact that there are over 400 now. This is often used as "proof" that mankind's industrial activity has caused the increase. Numerous studies have debunked this link between CO_2 and global temperatures.

measurements.[lxxvi, lxxvii] Their graphs show no increase in overall global temperature, but rather a DROP since satellite records began in 1979.[lxxviii]

Over the same period of time, a lab located high on Mauna Loa in Hawaii recorded the amount of carbon dioxide in the troposphere. Remember it's the amount of CO_2 that is meant to be causing an increase in temperatures. Well according to the NOAA Mauna Loa lab data records the percentage of CO_2 in the atmosphere has trended mainly upwards from the early 1960s until 2019 and continues to rise.[lxxix] So we have an increase in CO_2 PPM, yet the UHA satellite data shows that global temperatures have not increased at all since the late 1990s (and may even have dropped slightly). So again there is no established causation link between the two phenomena. This of course doesn't matter to the alarmist global media who gleefully proclaim:

"Earth's carbon dioxide levels are highest they've been in millions of years."

USA Today headline, June 4, 2019

Furthermore historical records produce the same results. This debunks the theory that atmospheric CO_2 concentrations result in increased global warming. For instance during the Roman and Medieval Warm Periods, where temperatures were higher [lxxx] than present, ice core and tree ring records show far less CO_2 than today.[lxxxi] Again showing there is NO link between the levels of CO_2 in the atmosphere and global temperatures at all.

The simple fact is, the myth about increased carbon dioxide creating higher temperatures has been proven incorrect numerous times.

Increased CO_2 is good for planet earth

Contrary to what you have been told, increased CO_2 is incredibly useful to our environment as higher concentrations of CO_2 increase crop yields and cause more plants to grow. Many commercial farmers purposely boost the CO_2 concentration levels in their green houses in order to increase the yield of their crops. And NASA satellite images show the increased greening over our planet, and certainly not less greening as radical environmentalists claim.

Conclusion

CO_2 is not a harmful pollutant at all, it's actually required for all life on earth to thrive. There is no proven link between increased levels of atmospheric CO_2 and warming. Lastly most of the increase seen in CO_2 levels is natural, not man-made or linked to any industrial activity at all.

10. Polar bears and climate change

Claim: The polar icecaps are melting and polar bears are in danger of extinction

"Polar bears are going extinct due to climate change!" "Melting polar ice means polar bears can't hunt and find food", "It's all our fault that polar bears are dying" and similar headlines have all been used numerous times to convince us that climate change is bad.

This is the message that the climate alarmist lobby has promulgated for years. Probably the most powerful example of this was a viral video from December 2017. The heart-wrenching clip showed a sick, old, frail polar bear on Baffin Island, Canada. In the video the dying bear is shown clinging to life. It is both tragic and difficult to watch.

It was widely reported that the thin, bony polar bear was dying of extreme hunger. It was reported that climate change had caused the arctic ice to melt and this poor polar bear couldn't catch any food. National Geographic and hundreds of other media outlets shared the video on their online platforms. And the images were shared hundreds of thousands of times via social media. These powerful images did what they were meant to do. Millions of people around the world were saddened, shocked and enraged. This incident clearly demonstrates how wildlife is often used to advance an environmental agenda.

The bare facts!

What didn't go so viral was the follow up and true back-story to this old polar bear. Scientists eventually corrected the original story and clearly stated that this particular bear was actually dying of old age. Its condition had nothing to do with climate change or being unable to find food at all. National Geographic [lxxxii] and some other sites corrected part of the story however millions never saw the correction. In their minds this poor, starving animal was dying because there was no ice and no food and it was all due to man-made climate change! Those powerful images and guilt stayed with us. We all felt sorry for the bear, but few learned the actual truth. In other words, a deceptive fake news report did its job. That's how environmental propaganda works and this is how most of the media report on climate change.

So what are real facts regarding polar bears? Is the global population of polar bears increasing or declining? It depends on whom you listen to.

Polar Bears International is an environmental group that focuses on everything to do with polar bears. They have a really cool website, lots of nice info and videos. They claim there are only 20,000 polar bears in the world today and this number is declining. Likewise the World Wildlife Fund has repeatedly proclaimed loudly that polar bear populations are declining due to climate change.[lxxxiii] Yet numerous biologists and researchers, many based in the Arctic Circle have published research showing that in fact polar bear populations are flourishing and not declining. Even Paul Nicklen, one of the biologists who filmed the staving polar bear video admits that polar bear populations around the

120

world are NOT in any danger. Data published in 2018 showed there were nearly 30,000 polar bears in the wild. This is the highest number in decades. So apparently the current environment is working for polar bears and not against them, despite all the ominous warnings from environmental groups.

Yet this hasn't stopped environment groups flooding the Internet with materials claiming the opposite. A typical example is an online video titled *"Are Polar Bears really going extinct?"* This video claims that polar bears *"can only handle a little bit of time without ice as it's very difficult for them to find enough food without it."*

Too many people simply accept at face value that polar bears are in danger. But it's not the truth. Polar bears are apex predators. And they have survived and adapted through warmer and colder periods before. Yes, their diet consists largely of the seals they catch on the frozen ice. However, and this is important, they are very resourceful. They can and will eat just about anything they can catch or find. This includes carrion, such as whale carcasses, small land animals, bird eggs, blueberries and more. And frozen sea ice or not, they still find plenty to eat.

This is borne out by Zoologist Dr. Susan Crockford, a world-renowned expert on polar bears, in her 2018 State of the polar bear report:

"We now know that polar bears are very resourceful creatures. They have made it through warm periods in the past and they seem to be taking the current warming in their stride too."

"The people of Nunavut[29] (in northern Canada) are not seeing starving, desperate bears – quite the opposite. Yet polar bear specialists are saying these bears are causing problems because they don't have enough sea ice to feed properly. The facts on the ground make their claims look silly, including the abundance of fat bears. Residents are pushing their government for a management policy that makes protection of human life the priority." [lxxxiv]

Conclusion

The bottom line is polar bears are doing just fine. Their numbers are increasing. This is simply another attempt to use a furry creature to promote an emotional response in order to sell climate change. Apparently no one told the polar bears they were going extinct!

---

[29] Baffin Island where the frail, dying polar bear video was filmed is in the Canadian territory of Nunavut.

11. Coral reefs and climate change

Claim: An increase in sea temperature from climate change is killing the world's coral reefs

Coral reefs are found all over the world's oceans. These large underwater structures are made-up of calcium carbonate exoskeletons of marine corals. Coral reefs are like the rain forests of the oceans and as any scuba diver knows, coral reefs team with life. They act as nurseries for all kinds of marine fish, plants and other sea life.

"Coral Reefs could be gone in 30 years. World heritage reefs will die of heat stress unless global warming is curbed, a new UN study finds."

National Geographic headline, June 23 2017 [lxxxv]

Climate scaremongers understand that most people are fascinated by and instinctively want to protect these colorful living eco-systems. Any threat to coral reefs draws a strong emotional response. Playing to this, environmentalists regularly use coral reefs to promote their cause. Claims that reefs "are dying", are "beyond repair", will "all be lost" due to

123

"climate change" are standard in the media when ever a coral bleaching event [30] occurs.

The fact is sea corals can be damaged and coral bleaching events have a variety of causes. And while these can include temporary rapid rises in sea temperatures there are numerous other causes. Some include; marine pollution, agricultural pesticides and fertilizers, oil and gasoline, sewage discharge and sediment from eroded land to predation and naturally occurring coral diseases, which damage and kill corals. Additionally, unethical fishing practices, including blasting with explosives and spraying cyanide to stun and catch fish, contribute to the destruction of fragile coral reef eco-systems. Even unseasonably colder than normal water temperatures can cause major damage to coral reefs. This is what happened in the Florida Keys in January 2010. [lxxxvi] Temperatures dropped 12 °F lower than normal, resulting in cold-stress and death to large parts of the warm water coral reef. Yet while the damage was extensive, the reef has since totally recovered.

All of this is well documented. Yet despite this widespread knowledge that there are multiple different causes for coral bleaching and damage, these tend to be downplayed or ignored in favor of blaming "climate change".

And despite the predictable dire media headlines that follow such events, the majority of coral reefs can and do recover on their own. In 2016 and 2017 large parts of the Great Barrier Reef were damaged and bleached. This is nothing new as coral bleaching on the Great Barrier Reef has been reported going back decades. The 2016 and 2017 bleaching events were naturally claimed to be caused by

---

[30] Coral bleaching occurs when coral is stressed or damaged and the algae plants that give the coral their color, either leave or are damaged. Coral bleaching events occur on a regular basis, however most coral reefs recover over time.

higher than normal surface temperatures. Apocalyptic headlines and nature documentaries declared that the coral reefs wouldn't survive, and this was the new normal. Fortunately the corals themselves didn't get the memo, as over the next few months following each bleaching, the reefs came back to life. Newsweek magazine even exclaimed:

"The Great Barrier Reef is better able to heal itself than we previously imagined!" [lxxxvii] November 29, 2017

Jennifer Marohasy, an Australian scientist and author is an outspoken critic of climate alarmism. She visited sections of the Great Barrier Reef and has written how most of the reports of coral bleaching damage were exaggerated. She dived and flew drones to check the conditions of the reefs to confirm her findings. She says the widely reported coral catastrophe was totally overblown and blames journalists who simply print and repeat stories without checking them. [lxxxviii]

Lastly there are many sea coral restoration projects, where lab grown live corals are literally "planted", and have proven that it's certainly possible to restore damaged coral reefs. This is now happening on numerous reefs worldwide.

Conclusion

I think we can safely conclude that all the ocean's coral reefs will not be destroyed by climate change!

The world's oceans and coral reefs face many environment challenges. Coral bleaching events may even look terrible but coral eco-systems are more resilient than previously thought and most reefs can and do recover. Environmentalists will continue to claim that global warming is driving coral reefs to extinction, but the evidence clearly shows otherwise.

12. Sea levels and climate change

Claim: Rising sea levels are a growing threat to coastal communities and cities

"There is no rapid sea-level rise going on today, and there will not be."

Dr. Nils-Axel Mörner, sea level subject matter expert and former UN IPCC scientist

Climate change advocates have long predicted global sea level rises of anywhere between 5 and 30 feet over the next century. Some of the more extreme reports claim that most of the eastern seaboard of the United States will be underwater by 2050. [lxxxix] That's just 30 years away. This is the newest and more recent target. It is important to note that several dates for rising sea levels have already been missed, and still no major permanent coastal flooding has actually occurred. That's the way most of these environmental predictions turn out. Nothing happens because they are totally inaccurate.

The "science" this claim is based upon is that of thermal expansion. This is water expanding as the oceans get warmer. This is in addition to claimed melting polar icecaps and glaciers, which will release fresh water into the oceans resulting in rising tidal seawater. Panic will follow as whole communities flee uninhabitable flooding cities and move inland. Bad news if you live in Miami, New York, Los Angeles or Seattle, which according to numerous rising seas reports, are all soon to be underwater. [xc, xci]

A November 2019 Fox News headline boldly proclaimed: *"Sea levels to keep rising even if humanity hits climate targets, scientists warn."* [xcii]

So how much truth is there behind all the scary headlines? Like most environmental claims, there is some truth and a lot of unfounded speculation. The fact is that sea levels have risen and fallen pretty much for all of recorded human history. This is nothing new and it certainly isn't tied to human industrial activity. Sea levels in some areas were rising long before the industrial revolution. Climate alarmists know this, they just conveniently ignore this truth, as it doesn't fit their narrative. Claiming that major cities will be underwater sounds so much more dramatic than explaining the facts.

So what does an actual sea level expert with over 50 years studying the issue say? Former UN IPCC scientist and a subject matter expert, Dr. Nils-Axel Mörner, says the United Nations are misleading everyone. In numerous interviews he has called out those claiming the seas are rising.

"There is no rapid sea-level rise going on today, and there will not be." he said, citing observable data.[xciii] His 2007 book, 'The Greatest Lie Ever Told', refers to his belief that observational records of sea levels for the past 300 years show variations - ups and downs, but no significant trend.[xciv]

Let's look at some other basic truths regarding sea levels.

The earth's crust is not static. Tectonic plates float on lower layers. When one plate rides up against another, it causes an earthquake. However, plates can also tilt overtime, causing land and seawater levels to rise and drop naturally.[xcv]

Land also sinks and rises naturally. There are many areas in the world and in the United States where land and cities are slowly subsiding [31] giving the impression the seas are rising. Many parts of Louisiana for instance, including most of New Orleans are slowing sinking. Additionally, coastal erosion is causing a loss of Louisiana coastland. The earth's crust under the coastland is being depressed by sediment collection in the Mississippi Delta; this causes the land to slowly sink as water is squeezed out of the land beneath. [xcvi] Land subsistence is not only a coastal issue. Large parts of inland California, Florida, Texas and other states have also sunk. None of this is due to climate change at all, but is rather the continuation of a long-term trend going back over many decades.[xcvii]

Lastly using US Geological Survey (USGS) topographic maps from the 1950s, and comparing them to current records does not show any rise in sea levels at all. For instance using government maps of Miami, which is one of the cities forecast by climate alarmists to be flooded, no sea level rise can be seen over the last 70 years. [xcviii]

---

[31] Land subsidence is a gradual settling or even sometimes sudden sinking of the earth's surface owing to subsurface movement of earth materials. Subsidence is a global problem, and in the United States, more than 17,000 square miles in 45 States, an area roughly the size of New Hampshire and Vermont are directly affected by subsidence.

Conclusion

There is little evidence to support rising sea levels as many claim. And even if the worse came to pass, the rise predicted by climate alarmists, (even by their extreme forecasts), is set to take place over the next century or longer. So any talk of a coming panic as coastal areas are flooded is simply ridiculous.

Furthermore modern sea storm flood technology could easily be developed and deployed if required. Consider the Netherlands where one-third of the land is below sea level. The sea is held back by sea dyke technology, which was developed over 400 years ago. If sea levels really started to rise, the rate would be very gradual, giving cities more than enough time to take action. And many countries with low lying lands and coastal cites are already busy deploying flood defenses to deal with the small, naturally occurring changes in sea levels as land sinks or rises.

13. Animal and plant extinctions

Claim: Climate change will cause massive animal and plant species extinctions to take place

Moving beyond the false claims that polar bears and coral reefs are dying off (neither are, see sections already covered), climate change scaremongers have doubled down on their dire pronouncements. They now increasingly claim that climate change will lead to a massive extinction crisis. This they assert will be the sixth mass extinction[32] in the history of the planet. [xcix]

And while climate change is most often blamed for the loss of biodiversity, in reality habitat loss and over-harvesting from the wild are the main reasons species go extinct. Trying to tie climate change to animal extinctions is a cheap PR trick designed to evoke an emotional response. There is simply no accuracy to this myth at all.

---

[32] Secular evolutionists, in their attempt to explain the creation of the millions of fossils found throughout the world and the disappearance of large dinosaurs have created a series of so-called "mass extinction" events. They claim these took place over the last 500 million years. The Biblical account of the worldwide flood during the time of Noah is a full and better explanation of the real world evidence of fossils.

The truth is animal and plant species have been lost to extinction since time began, and this is nothing new. Thus blaming climate change for something that has happened through history is a mass distortion of the facts. While Noah may have taken representatives of every kind of animal onto the Ark, the world they experienced after the flood was vastly different to the one before the global flood.

We know from the fossil record that many families of animals and multiple individual species didn't make it to the present. Sabre toothed tigers, woolly mammoths and numerous large and small dinosaurs were wiped out long before Jesus walked on the earth. In more recent times we have lost the dodo, the passenger pigeon, great auks, giant fossas, the quagga, Tasmanian tigers[33] and dozens of lesser-known species of birds, fish, small mammals, rodents and reptiles.

Currently thousands of different species and sub-species of animals are listed as critically endangered by IUCN (the International Union for the Conservation of Nature), an international organization that tracks the population size, range, habitat and conservation status of the world's wildlife. The vast majority face threats, but none are related to climate at all. By far the biggest threat is habitat loss.

Of all animal types alive today, amphibians are probably under a greater threat of extinction than any other. But again rather than climate change, the threat they face comes from

---

[33] Tasmanian Tigers or Thylacine were declared extinct in 1936. Over the years there have been reports of sightings in the wild. Despite this none have been confirmed.

habitat destruction, environmental pollution and a virulent form of deadly fungal disease, chytridiomycosis.[34]

Conclusion

There is no current mass biodiversity extinction underway. And while it's true we are losing some species, as we have since the beginning of time, other new species are being discovered at an increasing rate. In 2018 over 270 new species[c] were discovered by scientists. And in 2019 there were at least 71[ci] with many more still to come.[35] So no, climate change is not responsible for mass animal or plant extinctions at all.

---

[34] Chytridiomycosis is blamed for the greatest lose of biodiversity in modern times with at least 200 frog species either now extinct or on the way with rapid decline in numbers in the wild.

[35] The process of defining a new species typically involves description, DNA results, comparative studies and finding a journal to publish the description.

14. Renewable energy

Claim: "Renewable energy" is claimed to be cleaner, cheaper and more abundant than any other energy source

The central demand from all climate activists is the call for society to go "carbon neutral". They want to ban all fossil fueled energy sources, which currently supply over 90% of the U.S. and world's energy needs. And they demand a switch to what they claim are "cleaner, cheaper and unlimited renewable" sources of energy. The assumption being that fossil fuels are "dirty", contribute to climate change and are harmful to the environment, while "renewable energy" is not.

The green future envisioned by climate change promoters can be seen in futuristic movies, energy and car commercials. These show everything powered by solar panels and giant wind turbines with electric powered cars, trucks and even planes zooming about. So how realistic is the renewable powered future we have all been told we have to move to? Is it backed by real science or is it a fantasy? And is renewable energy really as clean, cheap and abundant as Hollywood and the commercials suggest? It sounds wonderful, so let's get into the facts!

Environmental impact

Firstly, lets correct the faulty misunderstanding regarding the impact on the environment. ALL energy sources have a byproduct.

They ALL impact the environment INCLUDING "renewable" energy sources. For instance many of the battery components of electronic powered vehicles are mined in poorer nations where they have a great environmental impact.[36] They are then shipped across the world in fossil fueled planes or ships and often manufactured in factories that use fossil fueled energy. Throughout their life cycle electric powered vehicles are mostly charged entirely via fossil fueled power grids. And at end of life, most are dumped into landfills. So despite the commercials, electric powered cars are not the clean environmental option most think they are.

Likewise wind and solar powered energy solutions have a large environmental impact, during manufacture and at end of life. And they all require fossil fueled back-up systems in order to keep working.

Renewable energy is not predictable, reliable or cheap

Renewable energy production is notoriously unreliable. Wind turbines only work when the wind blows and solar only when the sun shines. Both require massive battery backup arrays. Conversely coal, natural gas and nuclear powered energy plants work irrespective of the outside weather or of

---

[36] Over 60% of the world's cobalt, a major component of electric vehicle batteries, comes from the Democratic Republic of Congo (DRC), a nation with very poor human rights/child labor protection laws and environmental record.

the time of day making them far more effective and reliable as a modern energy source.

Wind turbines have the additional problem when the wind blows too hard, they have to be taken offline or risk the motors burning out. Newer systems typically have a maximum or rated power speed of between 30 and 55 miles per hour. If the wind blows faster, this triggers the wind turbine to automatically cut out.

Solar panels on the other hand capture sunlight and convert it to energy. To ensure solar powered systems stay operational battery backup systems are required. Even with these in place, the problem is unless the sun shines again, after the battery backups are drained of their power, the system shuts down. So a connection to conventional fossil fuelled power-grid is the only answer to providing a really reliable renewable energy source!

The absurdity of the battery backup solution becomes apparent as renewable energy projects scale up. The economics of adding massive battery backups for industrial solar projects, especially when the backups might only be needed for several days a year are becoming clear.

Even in Australia, one of the sunniest countries in the world, large-scale solar renewable power production is far more expensive than coal powered energy plants.[cii]

Renewable energy is not totally clean or environmentally friendly

Wind turbines

Wind turbines are notoriously bad for local wildlife and the environment. These huge wind powered turbines have some serious downsides to them.

Firstly wind turbines are not quiet. The huge blades of modern wind turbines are larger than the wing of a Boeing 747. As they spin they produce high levels of noise pollution. This is a major reason no one wants large wind turbines in their neighborhood. Even farmers don't want wind turbines near their livestock as the noise causes great stress to their animals.

They also cause enormous environmental damage as the massive spinning blades kill huge numbers of birds and bats.[ciii] The outer tips of large turbine blades can reach speeds of 180mph (288kph) and easily slice the wings off birds and bats that venture too close to them. Eagles, hawks and other birds of prey all too frequently fall victim as they look down when flying and don't see the huge spinning blades that shred them in mid-air. Even when erected away from land, wind turbines decimate seabirds.

It's estimated that over 500,000 birds[37] are killed annually in the United States by wind turbine blades. This includes many federally protected species such as bald and golden

---

[37] The exact number of birds killed is unknown as the wind industry hides as much data on bird strikes as possible from the public. Many wind energy providers will even sue to stop the true facts coming out.

eagles and other raptors. [civ] And despite pledges by manufactures to build in safety measures to prevent bird strikes, most experts including the Audubon Society[cv] believe wind turbines will never be safe for birds of prey or bats. And as new wind turbines continue to be added every year, millions more endangered birds will be injured or killed. The latest bird species to be threatened by wind turbines are critically endangered whopping cranes. [cvi]

Furthermore if noise pollution and wildlife damage were not enough, the massive wind turbine blades used to produce wind-powered electricity need to be replaced on a regular basis and they can't be recycled. Most power utilities are quickly finding this is a bigger problem than they realized.[cvii]

Wind turbine blades are huge and difficult to transport. They are made of fiberglass, resin and steel so can't be recycled and as they are built to withstand hurricane force winds, crushing them is difficult. The current solution is to dump thousands of massive toxic fiberglass blades into landfills. And most landfills are too small to handle blades as long as a football field. Moreover the recycling problem will only grow worse as more blades are retired and replaced each year.[cviii] Wind energy it turns out, is hardly a green solution at all!

The business side is equally bad. The lifespan for wind turbine blades is closer to 10 – 12 years, not the 25 plus years the wind industry claims. Consequently the renewal and disposal costs are higher than expected.[cix]

Lastly wind energy farms don't run on free wind power, they run on subsidies.[cx] Cut the subsidies and most wind powered energy production will grind to a halt as the production costs add up.[cxi]

Solar energy

While there are certainly some areas where solar power makes sense, off-grid for instance. But solar power is not as green, cost effective or practical as its proponents make it out to be either.

Firstly solar panels are still not very effective. They take up an enormous amount of space in relation to the amount of energy they produce. Industry figures of 15% to 22% energy conversion are used and that's the best case.

And solar panels are also not as environmentally friendly as their PR suggests. During manufacture a huge number of toxic and hazardous materials are used. These include gallium arsenide, copper-indium-gallium-diselenide, hydrochloric acid, sulfuric acid, nitric acid, hydrogen fluoride, 1,1,1-trichloroethane, and acetone. In many 3rd world countries where solar panels are produced, these materials end up being dumped into nearby fields and streams polluting water, poisoning people and the environment.[38]

Then there are the longevity and end-of-life disposal issues to consider. As time passes the performance of all solar panels degrades. Anywhere from 0.5% to 0.10% per annum is claimed. This means that at some future date, all have to be replaced and the old panels safely disposed of. While well-maintained solar panels can last anywhere from 10 up to 25 years[39] this is speculation as very few have been installed for

---

[38] In the United States, manufactures are required to make sure these substances are recycled rather than disposed of. In most Asian countries, very little regulation exists or is enforced.

[39] Some solar panels may well last as long as manufactures claim, but if wind energy is anything to go by they probably

that period of time. So typical-use-degradation rates are not as well established as manufactures claim they are[cxii]. When solar panels reach end-of-life, most end up as hazardous electronic waste. And because they contain toxic heavy metals such as cadmium and lead, if not disposed of correctly they can contaminate the environment. This environmental contamination is another growing problem that many climate change activists would rather ignore.

And while the solar industry makes claims of a future used solar panel "100% recycling boom", this may or may not happen. Most countries and states have few to no regulations or the required recycling facilities in place. And no one seems to have worked out if it will even be economically viable[40] to recycle the massive number of end-of-life solar panels in the next few years. Of course this may all change in the future, but for now, most damaged or old solar panels end up as semi-hazardous landfill waste.[cxiii]

Is it realistic to go without fossil fuel?

Another part of the green energy myth that needs to be exposed is the belief that we can simply stop using fossil fuels and switch to an alternative without any repercussions. The majority of those who think this way, I believe have no idea

---

won't. Other parts of the system such as batteries and inverters typically need to be replaced every 5 – 10 years.

[40] The difficulty with recycling solar panels isn't that the materials they are made from are hard to recycle; rather, it's that they are constructed from many parts all used together in one product. Separating those materials and recycling them each in a unique way is complex, expensive and nearly impossible.

how dependent our society really is on energy and products derived from fossil fuels. Climate activists have done a good job of creating a false narrative that society can simply rip out and replace one energy source they don't like, "fossil fuels" and replace it with another they do like, "renewable energy". The true picture is much more complicated.

We use oil, coal and natural gas for transportation, to heat and cool our homes, and to power industry. In addition there are over 6,000 everyday products derived from fossil fuels. These include asphalt for roads, fertilizer, perfumes, insecticides, soaps, vitamin capsules, detergents, paints, most modern household furniture, most modern textiles, clothes, shoes, kitchenware and much more. The list is ever expanding. Eliminating oil-based products out of modern life is simply impossible unless you want to go and live in a cave. The absurdity of the idea is totally lost to our modern day climate evangelists. If they had even the slightest idea of what they would have to give up, the majority of them would probably change their minds very quickly. Of course over time many could try and find alternatives but that takes time and money, which in most cases would bring no economic benefits. This is rarely spoken about.

The financial impact

Let's look at the financial impact. The oil and gas industry is a major source of jobs and revenue to the United States economy. It accounts for approximately 4% of all jobs (6.7 million people)[cxiv] with total revenues of around $181 billion per annum.[41]

---

[41] 2018 numbers, which were the latest reported.

In many individual states, the production, refining and distribution of oil and gas are a major growth industry. While every state in the Union has energy industry related employment, the states most heavily dependent on the energy sector include North Dakota, Texas, Wyoming, Colorado, Utah, New Mexico, Kansas, Pennsylvania, West Virginia, Oklahoma, Louisiana, Alaska, California and Ohio. Any attempts to ban or do away with fossil fuels would have major financial repercussions for these states. This would impact local economies with job losses, and also with a loss of state tax revenues.[cxv]

The effect on national economies

Another economic consequence to consider is that most of the world's oil underpins the economies of vulnerable parts of the world. In many of these countries there really isn't a lot of other industry. Stopping oil production would plunge large parts of the volatile Middle East, Russia, parts of Africa and South America into chaos, and back into poverty. Most climate activists and politicians with their comfortable Western lifestyles avoid this topic all together. If it is addressed at all, it's with the vague claim that new industries shall arise. The reality is that this will take time and investment dollars. It's a huge challenge with no clear-cut answers. In the meanwhile and for the foreseeable future, fossil fuel based economies can't be displaced without huge destabilizing circumstances, resulting in poverty that will affect millions of people.

Even in the most advanced economies, renewable power can't compete with fossil fueled power production. It's total fantasy to believe that abundant coal, oil and natural gas, which power 98% of the world's energy production, can simply be replaced without destroying the modern world economy.

Germany is a good example. In 2011 the left leaning Green political movement, riding the anti-nuclear wave after the Fukushima disaster in Japan, pressurized the German government to make a commitment to close all of its 17 nuclear reactors by 2022.[cxvi] The government and radical greens all claimed renewable wind and solar energy was the answer to providing zero-carbon electricity. So how has that worked out for Germany?

Well not as expected. Firstly, Germany has vastly increased its usage of wind and solar power to produce energy. By 2015 nearly one-third of the country's electricity was produced from wind and solar sources. However, even with all the wind and solar infrastructure, Germany's industrial carbon emissions have risen. Coal power plants are still needed to provide capacity.[cxvii] Additionally, as the wind doesn't blow all the time and solar is not an option at night or in cloudy weather, Germany can't produce enough power for their needs. They now buy in power from surrounding countries power grids, which is mostly produced by coal or nuclear power stations. To add insult to injury, today German citizens pay the highest cost for electricity in Europe,[cxviii] which is approximately 3 times the cost the average US household pays.[42]

We are seeing the same occur in some US states where power utilities have rolled out renewable power solutions. University of Chicago economists calculated that *"consumers*

---

[42] Germany has the highest electricity costs in Europe, with a rate of around 35 US cents per kilowatt-hour. Average US electricity rate is 12.69 cents per kilowatt-hour.

in the twenty-nine states that use the most renewable energy, paid $125.2 billion more for electricity than in those that don't use green energy". [cxix]

And in Virginia, in the midst of the state imposed coronavirus lockdown, far-left Democratic governor Ralph Northan enacted new state legislation committing Virginia power companies to becoming *"carbon free by 2045."* [cxx] While everyone was focused on other issues he imposed his new radical "clean energy" regulations by passing the Virginia Clean Economy Act. Maybe he should have looked at how similar legislation has worked out for Germany and California.

Conclusion

If the most advanced nations on earth can't make solar and wind energy production work for them, how are less technology advanced nations supposed to make green power work for them? And herein lies the problem; radical environmentalists and socialist loving politicians have no answers.

It's a fantasy to believe any nation can afford to cut off fossil fuel usage and not go back to the Middle Ages. Maybe at some future stage, when solar energy and battery storage technology is vastly improved then just maybe this might happen. But we probably won't see this happen for many years to come. In the meanwhile clueless politicians make stupid commitments to go "carbon neutral" without having any plan on how to get there. They are not being truthful, knowing full well that it's not an economically viable option. Claiming otherwise is pure propaganda and pandering, not truth.

Many politicians want the support of the masses, and have their own agenda. We see them make hollow political promises, instead of explaining the harsh economic reality of the "carbon free future". Most renewable energy projects are more about government policy than about protecting the environmental.

15. Weather records

Claim: It's the hottest day ever recorded

Media headlines proclaim on a regular basis that it's the hottest day or week or month on record. Yet whenever there is record cold weather, snowfall or wind-chill, it's just reported as abnormal weather. If however there is a "record" warm day, week or month in any location, that's always evidence of "climate change". Such is the duplicity with which the media report the weather.

We must understand that the majority of journalists simply report and say whatever they think will get them the most clicks and views, often in-line with their worldview.

Measuring the weather

In order to put claims of record warm weather into perspective, it's important to understand how weather records are measured.

Before the age of satellite weather records, there were many recording errors. Numerous recording stations were located in cities where building and industrial activity contributed to artificially high temperature readings. Human error also contributed to abnormal readings being recorded. But lets assume we accept historical measurement records as accurate. The hottest day on earth ever recorded was nearly 100 years ago in 1922 at a weather observatory in El Aziza, Libya with a reported high of 136.4 °F/58 °C. That record has been widely accepted in metrological circles as being accurate.

Incidentally the 2nd hottest recorded temperature accepted by weather scientists was actually over 100 years ago. On July 10, 1913 a weather observation post in aptly named, Furnace Creek in California recorded 134 °F/56.6 °C.[cxxi]

Note both of these record breaking high temperatures were recorded well before the current high levels of atmospheric CO_2. So obviously something else was responsible for the record heat and not the amount of CO_2 in the atmosphere.

Additionally, when making record temperature claims, climate change scientists totally ignore historical warmer periods, like the Medieval Warm Period, and colder periods, such as the Little Ice Age. Both of which they attempt to erase from history via social media scrubbing[43] and adjusting recorded temperatures in scientific journals. To their credit, if you read most record temperature claims carefully, many state "since record keeping began" which they usually start from

---

[43] Social media scrubbing is the act of social media censorship either by removing records or flooding the Internet with new data and misinformation that creates the desired narrative and effectively hides the data you don't want seen. Almost all technology platforms now engage in social media scrubbing and censoring of content that goes against their social views.

about century ago. And as we have already uncovered, a century ago was when the world was heating up and coming out of the last cold period. That cold period lasted from the late middle ages until the end of the 1800s or in some locations the early 1900s. When this context is added, current warming claims are not as spectacular.

Look at the list below. It shows record temperatures for many individual US states. As you will see by the date of each record, these temperatures were recorded long before Al Gore announced that increasing warm weather in the late 1990s would doom us all. As listed by the Weather Channel a few examples of warmest recorded state weather include: [cxxii]

Alaska,	100 °F/ 37.77 °C in 1915
Hawaii,	100 °F/ 37.77 °C in 1931
Maryland,	109 °F/ 42.77 °C in 1998
Missouri,	118 °F/ 47.77 °C in 1954
North Dakota,	121 °F/ 49.44 °C in 1936
Oklahoma,	120 °F/ 48.88 °C in 1936
Oregon,	119 °F/ 48.33 °C in 1898

Conclusion

As the record temperatures recorded above clearly show, current headlines proclaiming record warmest days are mostly incorrect. As an example in July 2019, The Washington Post wrote a sub headline, "Scientists say climate change is pushing Alaska's weather into record territory". [cxxiii] According to the article the temperature reached 90 °F at an airport in Anchorage. The article did not mention that this temperature was still 10 °F lower than the actual warmest recorded temperature from 1915! Yes, the weather was warm, but contrary to the headline, this is not proof of climate change. It was simply naturally fluctuating summer weather and way off the actual record.

16. There is no climate emergency

Claim: Climate change is a global "emergency"

"Most of the extremist views about climate change have little or no scientific basis."

Professor Gerd-Rainer Weber, German meteorologist

In order to promote the concept that climate change is an imminent threat to mankind, the United Nations IPCC decided (starting in December 2016) to re-frame climate change as a global "climate emergency". In a coordinated fashion taking their lead from the UN, various governments around the world followed. They announced "climate emergency declarations" along with proposed solutions to "fix the problem" and achieve "climate justice". Just to be clear, there was no new dire information that these new emergency declarations were based on. This was an attempt to double-down on previous climate claims. Many scientists disagreed with the UN pronouncement, claiming it was yet another attempt to gain traction using the same flawed data as before.

"The IPCC global warming model is not supported by the scientific data." [cxxiv]

Dr. Tom Segalstad, University of Oslo, Norway

At the September 2019 United Nations climate change summit, 500 well-qualified international scientists and engineers submitted a signed declaration stating:

"There is NO climate emergency". [cxxv.]

The declaration laid out the following:

- Nature as well as anthropogenic (man-made) factors cause warming
- Warming is far slower than predicted
- The current climate policies rely on inadequate climate models
- Carbon dioxide is "plant food, the basis of all life on earth" and not a threat
- Global warming has not increased natural disasters
- Climate policy must respect scientific and economic realities not governmental social agendas

<u>The UN ignored the scientists</u>. The scientific declaration didn't line up with the official, pre-determined UN climate change claims. Typical of the authoritarian organization it is, the UN is simply not open to anything that does not agree with their views.

The majority of the world's media, just like the UN IPCC themselves, ignore any data or accounts that don't agree with the official UN climate alarmist view.

"A global climate treaty must be implemented even if there is no scientific evidence to back the greenhouse effect."

Richard Benedik, President emeritus of the National Council for Science and the Environment and former U.S./U.N. bureaucrat

An example of how this works can be seen from the following 2019 press story taken from the BBC website. Most major news organizations ran with the same release and similar headlines.

The BBC headline read; *"UK Parliament declares climate change emergency"*. [cxxvi]

BBC News pitched this as a settled matter, portraying it as if the UK government had released the statement. Although in reality it wasn't the UK government, it was the opposition, far-left British Labour party making the statement. At this time the British government didn't make any such declaration so the headline was totally misleading. It seems nothing deters the alarmist BBC. They are true believers and a half-truth headline got their intended message out. Unless you actually read the details, anyone would get the false impression that the UK government had declared a climate emergency. A link to the headline above is also even included in the Wikipedia list of countries that have declared climate emergencies. As stated this was totally fake news. But to the millions of people who saw the headline and others like it, this was real proof of the actual dire emergency the world was facing. This is how the majority of the world's media produces and distributes what can only be called propaganda based on their political and social beliefs.

Not to be outdone, a few days later, the City of New York itself declared a climate emergency on its own. [cxxvii] Eventually a total of 670 city, state and national governments worldwide did the same after the UN made the first declaration. Even Pope Francis got in on the action, calling for "urgent action" as he likewise declared a climate change emergency. [cxxviii]

So what qualifies climate change as an emergency? Well according to the climate alarmists in media and academia almost any extreme weather or environmental news is offered as proof of climate change. That then is somehow blown out of proportion, often aided by computer climate models, which are seldom accurate. And this is exactly how the UN IPCC arrived at the place where they declared a climate emergency. So not very scientific, but then very little about climate change is actually scientific.

Climate change theory is mostly based on future climate models and predictions. These mostly get presented in a way that creates hysteria and panic. Because once enough people and governments are convinced that we do actually have an emergency of global proportion, who better to deal with it than the only form of global government we currently have, the United Nations themselves. And that is precisely the reason the UN have been so loud in promoting the climate change hoax throughout the world.

Conclusion

Declaring climate change an emergency was nothing more than a PR exercise to gain traction. The UN needs climate change to be seen as a global problem. This enables them to implement their radical social agenda to redistribute global wealth and control most of the world's economy.

Part 3: A Biblical view of nature

17. Our created world

"The heavens proclaim the glory of God. The skies display His craftsmanship."
Psalm 19:1 NLT

In the beginning God spoke the universe into being. The Creator could be seen in His creation. The planets in the night sky above display His glory. The vast diversity and variety of living creatures and plants do the same on the earth.

The book of Genesis describes the creation of the universe and our natural world. Rather than being the result of a random, unexplained "big bang", the universe and everything in it displays incredible design. When we look up into the night sky, even with the most powerful telescopes, we can only see a small fraction of the innumerable galaxies and the stars and planets they contain. David wrote in the book of Psalms that the heavens proclaim the glory of God and the skies above us display God's handiwork.

Likewise the Apostle Paul in Romans 1: 19-20 wrote that the truth about God is evident for all to see just by looking at the natural world around about us.

"They know the truth about God because he has made it obvious to them. For ever since the world was created, people have seen the earth and sky. Through everything God made, they can clearly see his invisible qualities—his eternal power and divine nature. So they have no excuse for not knowing God."

Romans 1: 19-20 NLT

So beyond creating a home for mankind to live in, the universe, the galaxies, stars and planets and everything in the natural world here on earth are a testament to God the creator. They all point to God, the same way a needle on a compass point to magnetic north.

One of the giants of science, biologist and chemist Louis Pasteur, is famous as the founder of immunology and pasteurization. He created the first vaccines for rabies and anthrax. His work disproved the evolutionary theory of spontaneous generation.[44]

Pasteur recognized God as creator proclaiming:
"The more I study nature, the more I stand amazed at the work of the Creator. I pray while I am engaged at my work in the laboratory."

He is not alone. Today many scientists have come to the same conclusion. They conclude that the natural world is wonderfully designed, and could never create itself as is taught by secular academics.

---

[44] Spontaneous generation is the theory that life originated from nonliving matter. The ancient Greeks were said to have first articulated it. The modern theory of macroevolution is built on the idea that spontaneous generation started life on earth.

18. Biblical stewardship

"The Lord God placed the man in the Garden of Eden to tend and watch over it."
Genesis 2:15 NLT

Adam was given the task of caring for and expanding the Garden of Eden. God made this clear in Genesis that mankind was given responsibility to care for, manage and subdue the natural world as owners with a stewardship responsibility.

In many progressive churches however, talk about stewardship of the earth is more aligned with how we should respond to climate change. They accept the environmentalists view of climate change as a proven fact. In doing so many interpret stewardship incorrectly. They take it to mean that we need to be focused on preserving nature and the environment as a goal in itself. Thus they agree with climate alarmist rhetoric and claims. While they are correct God gave us stewardship over His creation, stewardship does not mean we shouldn't use natural resources for the needs of mankind. And rather than focus their efforts on preserving nature, they should be focused on their main mission, to take the Gospel to their neighborhoods and make disciples!

Lets walk through this.

Ownership of the natural world

The Bible makes it very clear that God created the earth and it is His, by right of creation. David recorded this numerous times in the book of Psalms.

"The earth is the Lord's, and everything in it. The world and all its people belong to him. For he laid the earth's foundation on the seas and built it on the ocean depths."
Psalm 24:1-2 NLT

"For all the animals of the forest are mine, and I own the cattle on a thousand hills. I know every bird on the mountains, and all the animals of the field are mine. If I were hungry, I would not tell you, for all the world is mine and everything in it."
Psalm 50:10-12 NLT

"The heavens are yours, and the earth is yours; everything in the world is yours—You created it all."
Psalm 89:11 NLT

During the creation week in Genesis 1:26-28 God mandated that mankind should rule over the earth, subdue it and everything in it, and act as God's stewards or managers on the earth.

"Then God said, "Let Us make man in Our image, according to Our likeness; and let them rule over the fish of the sea and over the birds of the sky and over the cattle and over all the earth, and over every creeping thing that creeps on the earth. So God created man in His own image, in the image of God He created him; male and female He created them. God blessed them; and God said to them, "Be fruitful and multiply, and fill the earth, and subdue it; and rule over the fish of the sea and over the birds of the sky and over every living thing that moves on the earth."

Genesis 1:26-28 NLT

"You gave them charge of everything you made, putting all things under their authority."
Psalm 8:6 NLT

Psalm 8:6 confirms the stewardship role of mankind on the earth.

The definition of stewardship:

Stewardship (noun) is described as; the duties of a steward, a person who acts as the surrogate of another or others, especially by managing property, financial affairs, an estate, etc. And stewards are responsible for overseeing and protecting something considered worth caring for and preserving. That is mankind's role in the earth.

Untouched nature is not a Biblical concept

As stewards we should look after the environment, (that's good stewardship). And as already mentioned, conservation is good in the right context. However many people have the impression that untouched nature is how God intended the world to be. And that we should be careful to "preserve" it, and not use up too many raw materials. That is not a Biblical concept at all!

The earth is literally made-up of raw materials. And we are to use the natural resources that God has provided for us. Let's look at Genesis 1:27-28 again, this time in the Amplified classic version.

"So God created man in His own image, in the image and likeness of God He created him; male and female He created them.

And God blessed them and said to them, Be fruitful, multiply, and fill the earth, and subdue it [using all its vast resources in the service of God and man]; and have dominion over the fish of the sea, the birds of the air, and over every living creature that moves upon the earth."

Genesis 1:27-28 AMPC

God has put everything we will ever need into the earth. He is not sitting up in heaven concerned that mankind will run out of any natural resource before the world ends. And despite the shrill claims from environmentalists, God has commanded us to subdue the earth, *"Using all its (the earths) vast resources in the service of God and man".*

God has a people first worldview, not a creation and planet first policy. And that even includes using fossil fuels for energy production, cooking and heating if that's all that is available.

It's estimated that 1.2 billion people in poorer nations have no access to electricity.[cxxix] Restricting abundant coal would only drive them deeper into poverty. So while academics, the media and protesting student's call for bans on coal and fossil fuels, for many countries there simply are no economically viable alternatives. Of course this may change in the future, but until then imposing harsh measures that will hurt and impact the poor is evil, not good.

Now before anyone goes off on a tangent, I'm not suggesting we mine, log and indiscriminately exploit and destroy the entire planet. I'm a conservationist at heart. So of course we shouldn't trash our planet, that is not stewardship. Environmental pollution that destroys nature is inevitably bad for people as well. Adam was told to "work and keep" the

Garden of Eden. In other words, as a steward he was to use and work the natural resources God had provided.

We can use natural resources without over exploitation. It's possible to extract raw materials in a way that doesn't destroy and pollute waterways and the surrounding environment. It's possible to preserve natural parks where wild life can thrive and survive for future generations to enjoy, while at the same time building the roads, airports, cities and infrastructure we need for the world's current growing population. We are not to treat nature as sacred. We are to enjoy it, and to use the natural resources the Lord has abundantly provided for us responsibly and wisely. That's how stewardship is meant to work.

19. The coming kingdom

"The appearing of the Son of Man will burst forth with the brightness of a lightning strike that shines from one end of the sky to the other, illuminating the earth."
Matthew 24:27 TPT

The true Father heart of God is for people. From the very beginning, He planned to have a loving relationship with mankind. There is no hope in creation for people. What mankind needs is redemption. And because God loves people with a love so great that we can't comprehend, He wants everyone to make heaven.

John 3:16 points this out very clearly. For God (the Father, Son and Holy Spirit) SO LOVED the world (the people in the world, human beings), that He gave His only begotten Son (Jesus Christ), to come to earth to die on a cross for us, so that anyone who believes on and calls upon His Son, will be saved (have eternal life and become part of His family).

"For this is how God loved the world: He gave His one and only Son, so that everyone who believes in Him will not perish but have eternal life."
John 3: 16 NLT

So He provided redemption via Jesus taking our place and dying for mankind on the cross. And we need to be very clear on this. Jesus, didn't step out of eternity and become a man and live and die on earth to save the physical planet. And God is not sitting up in heaven worried about rising amounts of CO_2 in the atmosphere!

God cares about people and that's where our focus needs to be. The great commission is about making disciples of all nations, not saving the planet. Beyond reaching the lost and making disciples, we should be concerned with feeding the poor, stopping the murder of babies via abortion, caring for widows and the elderly. These are the things that move the heart of the Father. Much as we may care about nature and the natural world, the Word of God is unambiguous, that saving and caring for people first and foremost is what's important to God. That's where the primary focus of the church needs to be.

End time climate and events

"There will be famines and earthquakes in many parts of the world. But all this is only the first of the birth pains, with more to come."
Matthew 24:7-8

"And there will be strange signs in the sun, moon, and stars. And here on earth the nations will be in turmoil, perplexed by the roaring seas and strange tides. People will be terrified at what they see coming upon the earth, for the powers in the heavens will be shaken. Then everyone will see the Son of Man coming on a cloud with power and great glory. So when all

these things begin to happen, stand and look up, for your salvation is near!"

Jesus describing the signs before His return in Luke 21:25-28 NLT

The Bible clearly states before the return of the Lord, there will be severe natural disasters and wild weather on the earth. Additionally, the Bible describes unusual cosmic activity linked to the sun, moon and planets. Without getting into too much speculation, the Biblical accounts that Jesus mentions indicate the greatest natural disasters since the global flood in the days of Noah. And just like in the days of Noah, and the plagues in Egypt, God doesn't plan to bring judgment onto the righteous. Most of the accounts in the book of Revelation are reserved for those who rejects God's free offer of salvation and who follow the anti-Christ. Many of the worst judgments only occur after the rapture of the church.

How the world will end

"But the day of the Lord will come as a thief in the night, in which the heavens will pass away with a great noise, and the elements will melt with fervent heat; both the earth and the works that are in it will be burned up."

2 Peter 3:10

"All the stars in the sky will be dissolved and the heavens rolled up like a scroll; all the starry host will fall like withered leaves from the vine, like shriveled figs from the fig tree."

Isaiah 34:4

Ultimately our universe and planet will be burned up and remade by God. For the believer in Christ this should never been seen as bad, but rather part of the redemptive work of Christ when all things will be made new. Numerous Biblical passages detail the ending of our current physical world. An example is found in the book of Psalms. King David wrote not only of God creating our world, but also the certainty that our current earth and the heavens (the stars, galaxies and the universe) will eventually end and be replaced by something far better.

"With your hands you once formed the foundations of the earth and handcrafted the heavens above. They will all fade away one day like worn-out clothing, ready to be discarded, but you'll still be here. You will replace it all! Your first creation will be changed, but you alone will endure, the God of all eternity!"
Psalm 102:25 -26 TPT

Likewise, the prophet Isaiah saw forward into the future how the end of the earth would occur. His prophecy of total destruction is clearly recorded. This describes the coming judgment on the rebellious peoples of the earth and the fallen demonic hordes that influenced them:

"Destruction falls like rain from the heavens; the foundations of the earth shake. The earth has broken up. It has utterly collapsed; it is violently shaken. The earth staggers like a drunk. It trembles like a tent in a storm. It falls and will not rise again, for the guilt of its rebellion is very heavy.

In that day the Lord will punish the gods (demons) in the heavens and the proud rulers of the nations on earth. They will be rounded up and put in prison. They will be shut up in prison and will finally be punished.

Then the glory of the moon will wane, and the brightness of the sun will fade, for the Lord of Heaven's Armies will rule on Mount Zion. He will rule in great glory in Jerusalem, in the sight of all the leaders of his people."
Isaiah 24: 18b- 23 NLT

This combined with the apostle John's detailed description in chapter 21 of Revelation and Hebrews 12: 26 – 28 gives a very precise picture of the end of this current physical world and the new heaven and the new earth that Jesus will create.

"Then I saw a new heaven and a new earth, for the old heaven and the old earth had disappeared. And the sea was also gone. And I saw the holy city, the New Jerusalem, coming down from God out of heaven like a bride beautifully dressed for her husband.

I heard a loud shout from the throne, saying, "Look, God's home is now among his people! He will live with them, and they will be his people. God himself will be with them. He will wipe every tear from their eyes, and there will be no more death or sorrow or crying or pain. All these things are gone forever."

And the one sitting on the throne said, "Look, I am making everything new!" And then he said to me, "Write this down, for what I tell you is trustworthy and true." And He also said, "It is finished! I am the Alpha and the Omega—the Beginning and the End. To all who are thirsty I will give freely from the springs of the water of life. All who are victorious will inherit all these blessings, and I will be their God, and they will be my children."

Revelation 21: 1-7 NLT

"Now He has promised, saying, "Yet once more I shake not only the earth, but also heaven." Now this, "Yet once more," indicates the removal of those things that are being shaken, as of things that are made, that the things which cannot be shaken may remain. Therefore, since we are receiving a kingdom which cannot be shaken, let us have grace, by which we may serve God acceptably with reverence and godly fear."

Hebrews 12: 26 – 28 NLJV

Instead of looking forward in fear that the planet is doomed for destruction, we should rather be focused on fulfilling our mission as ones who will have to give an account to our King when He returns.

Conclusion

All mankind sinned in Adam; but all mankind was redeemed and set free in Jesus. The earth is our current home, that's all. It's a beautiful place but it's flawed and cursed due to sin. In the end, when Jesus returns He will create a new and perfect home for us, a new earth where we will live for eternity in harmony with nature. There is an amazing description of this in the 11th chapter of Isaiah.

In that day the wolf and the lamb will live together; the leopard will lie down with the baby goat.
The calf and the yearling will be safe with the lion, and a little child will lead them all. The cow will graze near the bear.
The cub and the calf will lie down together. The lion will eat hay like a cow. The baby will play safely near the hole of a cobra.
Yes, a little child will put its hand in a nest of deadly snakes without harm. Nothing will hurt or destroy in all my holy mountain, for as the waters fill the sea, so the earth will be filled with people who know the Lord.
Isaiah 11: 6-9 NLT

The new heaven and earth will be beyond anything we can imagine. Everyone who puts their trust and hope in Jesus Christ as their Lord and Savior will live for eternity is this wonderful place. I hope to see you there.

(See Appendix B, for how to receive eternal life)

Appendix A: Real environmental issues

I have always loved nature and am in awe of the creation we have been given. So I'm painfully aware that the health of our larger environment plays a crucial role in the continuing sustainability of life on earth, including human life. And while many environmental concerns are blown out of proportion, not all are.

The focus of this book has been to bring awareness of the issues and the misbeliefs behind the climate change movement. However, there are some real environmental issues that should concern us. As we have already pointed out, climate change is simply NOT one of them.

Fortunately the United States has some of the strongest environmental regulations in the world. As a result our rivers and air are cleaner than they have ever been.[cxxx] However, no amount of regulation can keep us healthy if we continue to eat food that is filled with antibiotics, sprayed with pesticides and contaminated by plastic pollution!

Real environmental issues: Plastic pollution

Plastic is a major growing cause of environmental pollution. An increasing amount of plastic waste ends up in oceans, rivers and almost every other eco-system around the globe.

Our throwaway "culture of convenience" has led to an explosion in the use of unregulated single-use plastic that is designed to be discarded after use. The problem is totally out of control. It's estimated that over half of all plastic products produced are used once, and then thrown away. Even much of what is recycled in wealthy nations is shipped to poorer nations. And a large amount of that plastic waste ends up polluting the receiving countries!

Plastic totally dominates much of the packaging industry. In food and beverage packaging, plastic to-go containers from restaurants along with plastic water bottles, caps and single-use bowls are fueling the growing waste problem. Apart from single-use plastic, the other worse offenders are plastic shopping bags, straws, balloons, chip bags and candy wrappers. And now with the coronavirus pandemic, there are millions of facemasks and plastic gloves ending up as more trash. So while plastic is incredibly useful, its misuse is really bad for the environment.

Micro-plastic particles

The problem is that plastic doesn't degrade well. When exposed to sun and salt water it simply breaks down into smaller micro-plastic particles. And all plastics contain toxic chemicals. So when fish, birds and marine animals eat micro-plastic particles, the toxins they contain become concentrated into the food chain. And ultimately many of those toxins end up on our plates.

A study conducted by Ghent University in Belgium concluded that the average European citizen who eats fish consumes 11,000 fragments of plastic each year. [cxxxi] It's unclear what the long-term health consequences of this will be. And as the rate of plastic pollution increases the problem will only get worse.

Here is an example of how wide spread the micro plastic pollution is. In a new Canadian study, conducted in November 2019, the stomach and intestine contents of 7 beluga whales were checked. These whales were living in an isolated area in far northern Artic waters. Micro plastic particles were found in every one of them. [cxxxii] This shows that fish consumed by these remote living beluga whales had either eaten the plastic particles themselves or had consumed other smaller marine organisms that had.

No one knows how much plastic the oceans contain, as much of it sinks to the ocean bottom. However, at this point it's fair to assume almost every corner of the world's oceans have been contaminated to some degree by plastic pollution. Studies have concluded that about eight million tons of plastic are added each year.[45] Which is in addition to the millions of tons already in the oceans. This has been likened to a garbage truck full of plastic being dumped each minute into the world's oceans. [cxxxiii] Clearly the environmental impact is huge and unsustainable.

The European Union is starting to place bans on disposable plastics and polystyrenes. The state of California plans to phase out single use plastics by 2030. Other states need to follow suite. While these efforts are admirable, in the

---

[45] This is the approximate weight of nearly 90 aircraft carriers.

short term they will do little to stem the tide, as the biggest plastic polluters are the rapidly urbanizing Asian nations of China, Indonesia, Vietnam, Thailand and the Philippines and Nigeria in Africa. Of the world's top 20 most plastic polluted rivers, 14 are in Asia.[cxxxiv] These plastic superhighways carry millions of tons of plastic into the world's oceans each year. Most developing nations have neither robust environmental protection laws nor the means to enforce those they do have.[cxxxv]

The problem has been further compounded by western nations who for years have shipped their plastic recycling waste to Asian nations. Fortunately the tide may start to turn a bit with some of these nations now banning the importation of recycled plastics from other countries. And while NGOs are aware and active in most plastic pollution epicenters, they are under funded and unable to stem the flood.

This would be a really good place to spend some of the $billions of that is wasted on climate change and make a real impact instead!

If western environmental activists really cared about the environment, they should switch their focus and energy to helping solve the plastic pollution problem instead of wasting time on the fantasy of climate change.

Take action

Rather than buy and discard plastic water bottles, use a refillable water container. Bottled water is not always healthier than filtered tap water. While marketing labels may show fresh mountain streams and glaciers, the reality is that there are less stringent purity tests for bottled water than for most water utilities. As reported by the Cleveland Clinic, studies have found numerous pollutants, chemical by-products and even bacteria in bottled drinking water. [cxxxvi] Filtered tap water is considered healthier and doesn't contribute to plastic waste.

While not all food stores offer bulk foods without the plastic packaging, many do. If possible purchase in bulk without the plastic bag. Likewise limit plastic bag usage by shopping with a reusable shopping bag or opt for paper if it's available.

And instead of buying fast-food/take-out everyday, which is probably not too healthy either, pack your own lunch in a reusable container. It will cost you less, be healthier for you and cut down on single use plastic waste.

Real environmental issues: Toxins in our food

Exposure to environmental toxins and the over usage of antibiotics are a proven cause of illness not only in humans but in animals as well. While the majority of people are aware of the environmental dangers of things like lead based paints and BPA plastic exposure, most are ignorant of the menace that pesticides, herbicides, insecticides and fungicides used in the production of most edible crops pose to their health.

Glyphosate

One of the most controversial toxins used on human food crops is the herbicide glyphosate. Glyphosate is the main ingredient in the weed killer Roundup, the most widely used weed killer in the world today.

Monsanto (now owned by Bayer) first introduced glyphosate in 1974. Since then it has found its way into almost every area of the crop farming industry. This includes into seeds and being sprayed onto food crops. In 2015, the World Health Organization found glyphosate to be "probably carcinogenic to humans" and numerous countries banned or limited its use. [cxxxvii] With competing claims, other international food and governmental agencies have concluded that glyphosate should not be classified as carcinogenic. There is no doubt many disagree with their conclusions due to the amount of money involved and the Bayer funded trails being used in the decision making process!

In a 2019 study of different popular food items,[cxxxviii] high levels of glyphosate were found in most of them even including some listed as organic.[cxxxix] It's easy to understand why. Over 250 million pounds of this poison is sprayed onto crops in American every year. This includes spraying fields of wheat, barley, oats and beans destined for human consumption. It's no wonder that food products made with these crops have been found to contain glyphosate. This includes breads, chips, crackers, cereals, biscuits, corn and even beer.

To date, more than 11,000 Roundup lawsuits have been brought against Monsanto and Bayer over non-Hodgkin's lymphoma and other alleged side effects of Roundup exposure. Millions of dollars in damages have already been awarded to plaintiffs in these cases. In 2016 groundskeepers and gardeners who had used Roundup for years and were diagnosed with Non-Hodgkin lymphoma, (a type of cancer which starts in white blood cells), filed the first of these US lawsuits. Other types of cancers linked back to pesticide usage include prostrate, ovarian, brain and breast cancers.

And while many lawsuits are still ongoing; this hasn't stopped commercial farmers who are still big fans of using glyphosate. Farming experts claim that modern commercial farms can't operate without glyphosate and many are not willing to get rid of it.[cxl] What they really mean is, the large industrial farms that use it won't make as much money as they do today, without it. Of course there are alternatives as has been proven by commercial farmers in Europe. However, they are not as effective at killing weeds, and require more work to apply them. So for now, unless you opt strictly for organic foods, you will be consuming glyphosate in the foods you eat.

Steven R. Gundry, MD, the director of the International Heart and Lung Institute in Palm Springs, California and a former distinguished professor and chairman of cardiothoracic surgery at Loma Linda University, has a lot to say about the dangers of glyphosate. He warns that consuming glyphosate kills beneficial gut bacteria, (which allows harmful bacteria to proliferate), disrupts our body's ability to produce several essential amino acids and can stop our liver's ability to convert vitamin D to its active form.[cxli] Numerous medical writers have linked leaky gut syndrome to glyphosate in the foods we eat.

And it's not just food crops that are covered in roundup. Livestock grown for food are fed grains containing glyphosate as well. The only way to avoid glyphosate is to eat, organic, grass fed meat.

Real environmental issues: Bee colony collapse disorder

There are numerous additional harmful environmental results from the overuse of pesticides and herbicides by commercial farmers. One of greatest concerns is that of bee colony collapse disorder [cxlii] where both neonicotinoid insecticides [46] and glyphosate [47] are key known contributors.[cxliii]

Throughout the world, honeybees are the single most important pollinator species in agriculture. They are essential in pollinating numerous food crops including almonds and almost 100 other nut species, as well as many fruits and vegetables. Bees are in high demand as pollinators for the beef and dairy industry as well where they pollinate clover, hay and other crops used to feed livestock.

Colony collapse disorder occurs when the majority of worker honeybees in a colony die off, leaving the hive without the means to feed itself. In 2016 researchers reported that honeybee keepers lost over 44% of their bee colonies. This was an increase from 42.1% in 2015 and 39% in 2014.[cxliv]

While there are numerous causes for colony collapse disorder, the overuse of pesticides and fungicides plays a large part.

---

[46] Neonicotinoids are a new form of insecticide, more toxic to insects than to mammals and birds. Some states have restricted their use in order to protect bees and other pollinators.

[47] While glyphosate doesn't directly kill honeybees, being exposed to glyphosate weakens their specialized gut microbiota and immune systems leaving them more susceptible to infection by opportunistic pathogens. The end result however is the same, dead bees.

Take action

Do everything possible to avoid products contaminated with glyphosate. Buy organic where possible and if you have the time and space consider growing some of your own foods.

There is also no need to poison the environment in your own yard, so avoid using Roundup. If you need to control weeds around your home, try using a nontoxic homemade weed killer. It's a safer and more environmentally friendly option. A vinegar and either salt or baking soda solution works equally as well as toxic pesticides. Even simple boiling water will kill weeds in driveways and paving.

To control sap-sucking bugs on your plants, there are numerous safer and homemade alternatives to spraying poisonous insecticides. A mixture of vegetable oil and mild soap in a hand spray bottle will get rid of most insects such as aphids, whiteflies and plant mites. Diatomaceous earth[48] acts as a natural pesticide. When added around plants it will stop slugs and snails. When sprinkled on leaves it will also kill plant mites, aphids, their larvae and crawling insects. Just don't forget to reapply after rain. Lastly remember many garden birds feed on insects, as do most bats in our country. So avoid using any kind of neonicotinoid products. A simple Internet search will turn up dozens of sites with instructions

---

[48] Diatomaceous earth is a power-like dust made from the silicate-fossilized skeletons of tiny ocean-dwelling creatures called Diatoms. It's mined from areas that were formally underwater and is available at most outdoor stores and online. It is safe for most animals but toxic to cockroaches, ticks, fleas, mites, bed bugs and other insect species.

on how to make and apply non-toxic weed killers and insecticides.

Appendix B: How to receive eternal life

"Everyone who calls on the name of the Lord will be saved."
Romans 10:13 NLT

If you don't yet know Jesus as your Lord and Savior and would like to, or if you are unsure of where you will spend eternity, I've got good news for you. God loves you and has a great plan for your life. Jesus Christ, the Son of God has already died on the cross and paid the price for all your sins. In order to ask Him to be your Lord and Savior say the following prayer with all sincerity.

"Dear Lord Jesus, I acknowledge that I have sinned. I ask you to forgive me, come into my heart and wash me clean. Help me to follow you. I believe you died for me and you will come back again. I accept you as my Lord and my Savoir and I will spend the rest of my life following you. In Jesus name, Amen."

After praying this, the Bible clearly states you are forgiven of all your sins and you have been born again. Welcome into the family of God! You are now a brand new creation, the old you has passed away. You are no longer lost for eternity, when you die you are on your way to heaven. This is how the Living Bible puts it:

"This means that anyone who belongs to Christ has become a new person. The old life is gone; a new life has begun!"
2 Corinthians 5:17 NLT

The next step is to find a Bible believing church and start to attend on a regular basis. It's important to hear good teaching and get to know God better. Get a Bible and read the New Testament.

If you prayed that prayer and have any questions, or would like us to pray with you, contact us at www.johnberryministries.com

Acknowledgements

I want to thank everyone who in one way or another contributed to the completion of this book.

Firstly, I acknowledge and deeply thank God as Creator for His incredible creation He made for us. Like King David in the book of Psalms, I'm in awe of the depth, beauty and variety of living creatures on planet earth, and the billions of planets in the universe. The creation truly reflects the magnificence of its maker.

I am also grateful to a number of family and friends who encouraged me to start and stick with this project and to finally publish it.

These include, my wife, Mary, for affording me the time to write this book. I wouldn't do this or most of my other writing without your support. Thank you for keeping me going.

Lastly to all those who helped with proof reading and providing feedback including, Ana Barrett, Lon McClelland,

Chad Williams and others for reviewing my manuscript, listening to my ideas and providing valuable feedback. I am grateful for your assistance and friendship.

Thank you all.

About the author

John Berry is an author, speaker, pastor and technologist.

A former atheist, he worked in both the herpetological (reptile biology) and software industries for over twenty-five years. He has traveled widely and lived and worked in the United Kingdom, South Africa, the Middle East and the United States, where he now resides. He divides his time between researching, writing, pastoring and various entrepreneurial technology projects.

Contact details:
www.johnberryministries.com
https://www.facebook.com/JohnBerryMinistries

Speaking engagements: To book John for a speaking engagement email us at johnberryministries@gmx.com

His teaching and topics can be tailored to the type of event that best fits your needs including Sunday Service / Youth Service / Men's Meeting / Out-Reach Event / Weekend Seminar or Workplace meeting, etc.

Topics include climate change, creation science/ debunking evolution, cultural and social issues. As well as other Biblical and Word of Faith topics.

Endnotes

Note: All online references were accessed and verified as correct and working when this book was written (late 2020). However, they are subject to change or deletion by the poster. If any links are not working, try searching using the name of the article for an alternative link.

---

[i] Simon Kent, *"Youth leaders tell UN to save the world, declare*
[ii] Edward Morgan, *"Al Gore, the worlds first 'carbon billionaire"* by profiting off irrational climate fears", March 22, 2018, https://prepareforchange.net/2018/03/22/al-gore-the-worlds-first-carbon-billionaire-by-profiting-off-irrational-climate-fears/
[iii] Marc Morano, *"Gore's quest to become fake meat billionaire",* https://www.climatedepot.com/2019/08/17/gores-quest-to-become-a-fake-meat-billionaire-lobbies-for-climate-policies-

that-limit-meat-while-his-firm-invests-200-million-in-meat-substitutes/

[iv] *"Renewable Energy Transition: Wind and Solar obsession leaves Germany suffering the worlds highest power prices"*, February 2, 2020, https://stopthesethings.com/2020/02/02/renewable-energy-transition-wind-solar-obsession-leaves-germans-suffering-the-worlds-highest-power-prices/

[v] Justin Haskins, *"Al Gore, UN Secretary-General, others now demanding "Great Reset" of global capitalism"*, June 24, 2020, https://www.foxbusiness.com/markets/al-gore-un-secretary-general-great-reset-global-capitalism

[vi] Frisia, S., Borsato, A., Spotl, C., Villa, I.M. and Cucchi, F. 2005. *"Climate variability in the SE Alps of Italy over the past 17,000 years reconstructed from a stalagmite record"*. Boreas 34: 445-455

[vii] Giraudi, C. 2009. *"Late Holocene glacial and periglacial evolution in the upper Orco Valley, northwestern Italian Alps"*. Quaternary Research 71: 1-8.

[viii] Livius, *"Caesar on the first Germanic campaign"*, https://www.livius.org/sources/content/caesar/caesar-on-the-first-germanic-campaign/

[ix] Neukom, R., Steiger, N., Gómez-Navarro, J.J. et al. *"No evidence for globally coherent warm and cold periods over the preindustrial Common Era"*. July 24, 2019, https://doi.org/10.1038/s41586-019-1401-2

[x] David Rose, *"Global warming stopped 16 years ago, reveals Met office report quietly released"*, October 16, 2012, https://www.dailymail.co.uk/sciencetech/article-2217286/Global-warming-stopped-16-years-ago-reveals-Met-Office-report-quietly-released--chart-prove-it.html

[xi] Valerie Richardson, *"Climate change whistleblower alleges NOAA manipulated data to hide global warming "pause"*, February 5, 2017, https://www.washingtontimes.com/news/2017/feb/5/climate-change-whistleblower-alleges-noaa-manipula/

xii Hisayo Takada, *"Abe's coal addiction"*, October 3, 2018, https://thediplomat.com/2018/10/abes-coal-addiction/

xiii Colorado Peak Politics reporter *"Non-violent protest? Climate change activists block traffic at their own peril"*, September 24, 2019, https://coloradopeakpolitics.com/2019/09/24/non-violent-protest-climate-change-activists-block-traffic-at-their-own-peril/

xiv Jessica Chasmar, *"Nancy Pelosi on wildfires: 'Mother Earth is angry"* September 11, 2020, https://www.washingtontimes.com/news/2020/sep/11/nancy-pelosi-on-wildfires-mother-earth-is-angry/

xv Adam Wernick, *"Environmental lawyers seek legal rights for the natural world"*, December 2, 2017, https://www.pri.org/stories/2017-12-02/environmental-lawyers-seek-legal-rights-natural-world

xvi *"Universal declaration of rights of mother earth"*, April 22, 2010, https://therightsofnature.org/universal-declaration/

xvii *"Climate Change Education"*, https://en.unesco.org/themes/education-sustainable-development/cce

xviii *"Climate confessions"*, https://www.nbcnews.com/news/specials/climate-confessions-share-solutions-climate-change-n1054791

xix James Delingpole, *"Forbes cancels environmentalist who wrote, 'I apologize for the climate scare"*, June 30, 2020, https://www.breitbart.com/politics/2020/06/30/delingpole-forbes-cancels-environmentalist-who-wrote-i-apologize-for-the-climate-scare/

xx David Rose, *"Climate crazies plan "public suicides" at next UN climate summit"*, March 13, 2020, https://climatechangedispatch.com/climate-crazies-plan-public-suicides-at-next-un-climate-summit

[xxi] Haley Ott, *"Millions hit the streets for global climate change strike"*, September 20, 2019, https://www.cbsnews.com/live-news/global-climate-change-strike-protests-today-2019-09-20-live-updates/

[xxii] Sky News, *"50 arrested as Melbourne climate protests turn violent"*, October 10, 2019, https://www.msn.com/en-nz/news/world/50-arrested-as-melbourne-climate-protests-turn-violent/ar-AAJvQfs

[xxiii] Rishi Iyengar, *"200 arrested amid violent protests at Paris climate talks"*, November 30, 2015, https://time.com/4129017/paris-protests-climate-talks-violent-arrests-200/

[xxiv] Travis Fedschun, *"Over foot of snow falls on Colo., Wyoming, breaks 70-yr record"*, June 10, 2020, https://climatechangedispatch.com/june-snowstorm-foot-snow-colorado-wyoming/

[xxv] Environmental Progress News, June 29, 2020, *"On behalf of environmentalists, I apologize for the climate scare"*, (as published in Forbes magazine), https://environmentalprogress.org/big-news/2020/6/29/on-behalf-of-environmentalists-i-apologize-for-the-climate-scare

[xxvi] Becky Yeh, *"7 incredibly shocking quotes from Planned Parenthood founder Margaret Sanger"*, February 23, 2015, https://www.lifenews.com/2015/02/23/7-shocking-quotes-from-planned-parenthood-founder-margaret-sanger/

[xxvii] *"Planned parenthood honors secretary of state Hillary Rodham Clinton for her commitment to woman's health care"*, January 30, 2014, https://www.plannedparenthood.org/about-us/newsroom/press-releases/planned-parenthood-honors-secretary-state-hillary-rodham-clinton-her-commitment-womens-health-c

[xxviii] Kevin Vance, *"Sec. Clinton stands by her praise of eugenicist Margaret Sanger"*, April 15, 2009, https://www.washingtonexaminer.com/weekly-

standard/sec-clinton-stands-by-her-praise-of-eugenicist-margaret-sanger

xxix Peter J. Smith, *"Obama science czar envisioned "Planetary Regime" of forced abortion and sterilization program"*, July 14, 2009, https://www.lifesitenews.com/news/obama-science-czar-envisioned-planetary-regime-of-forced-abortion-and-steri

xxx Jeffery D. Sachs, *"With 7 billion on earth, a huge task before us"*, October 21, 2011, https://www.cnn.com/2011/10/17/opinion/sachs-global-population/index.html

xxxi Les Knight, *"Experience: I campaign for the extinction of the human race"*, January 10, 2020, https://www.theguardian.com/lifeandstyle/2020/jan/10/i-campaign-for-the-extinction-of-the-human-race-les-knight

xxxii Dana McCauley, *"Church leaders use Christmas message to call for climate action"*, December 24, 2019, https://www.smh.com.au/politics/federal/church-leaders-use-christmas-message-to-call-for-climate-action-20191222-p53mau.html

xxxiii Tola Mbakwe, *"We really feel like we're following in the footsteps of Jesus": Christian wing of Extinction Rebellion gearing up for protests"*, August 28, 2020. https://premierchristian.news/en/news/article/we-really-feel-like-we-re-following-in-the-footsteps-of-jesus-christian-wing-of-extinction-rebellion-gearing-up-for-protests

xxxiv Church of England, *"The environment and climate change"*, https://www.churchofengland.org/environment

xxxv Lee Foster, *"United Methodist Church Statement on Climate change"*, September 2011, http://ncipl.org/wp-content/uploads/2013/03/United-Methodist.pdf

xxxvi Greg Garrison, *"Methodists: Punish pastors for denying global warming"*, June 5, 2019, https://www.al.com/life/2019/06/methodists-punish-pastors-for-denying-global-warming.html xxxvii Fiona Harvey, Jillian Ambrose, *"Pope Francis declares 'climate emergency' and urges action"*, June 14, 2019, https://www.theguardian.com/environment/2019/jun/14/pope-francis-declares-climate-emergency-and-urges-action

xxxviii *"Spreading the climate-gospel: The Rise of green churches"*, January 21, 2020, https://www.dw.com/en/green-gospel-climate-change-church-religion/a-51929960

xxxix Jon Brown, *"Absolute theological bankruptcy, Union Theological Seminary students confess climate change sins to plants"*, September 18, 2019, https://www.washingtonexaminer.com/news/absolute-theological-bankruptcy-union-theological-seminary-students-pray-to-plants

xl *"Climate change – prayers of confession, absolution and intercession"*, https://www.thesanctuarycentre.org/resources/written-prayers-prayers-in-response-to-climate-change.pdf

xli Rob Lyons *"The IPCC goes looking for bad news"*, April 23, 2007, https://www.spiked-online.com/2007/04/23/the-ipcc-goes-looking-for-bad-news/

xlii Cap Allon, *"The List – Scientists who publicly disagree with the current consensus on climate change"*, December 20,2018, https://electroverse.net/the-list-scientists-who-publicly-disagree-with-the-current-consensus-on-climate-change/

xliii Craig D. Idso, Robert M. Carter, S. Fred Singer, *"Why scientists disagree about global warming, 2nd edition"*, 2016, https://www.heartland.org/_template-assets/documents/Books/Why%20Scientists%20Disagree%20Second%20Edition%20with%20covers.pdf

xliv Mark Hodges, *"Climate change is "the biggest scientific fraud perpetrated"*, October 18, 2017, https://www.lifesitenews.com/news/climate-change-alarmists-disregard-sanctity-of-human-life-population-expert

[xlv] Professor Judith Curry *"Statement to the subcommittee on space, science and competiveness of the United States Senate"*, December 8, 2015, https://curryja.files.wordpress.com/2015/12/curry-senate-testimony-2015.pdf

[xlvi] Larry Bell, *"Global warming's tree ring circus brings us the costliest show on earth"*, February 4, 2014, https://www.forbes.com/sites/larrybell/2014/02/04/global-warmings-tree-ring-circus/#6829e2934774

[xlvii] Barbara Hollingsworth, *"Climate change for 18 years, "An orchestrated litany of lies"*, December 14, 2009, https://www.washingtonexaminer.com/climate-change-for-18-years-an-orchestrated-litany-of-lies

[xlviii] Marc Morano, *"MIT climate scientist Dr. Richard Lindzen rips UN IPCC report"*, September 28, 2013, https://www.climatedepot.com/2013/09/28/mit-climate-scientist-dr-richard-lindzen-rips-un-ipcc-report-the-latest-ipcc-report-has-truly-sunk-to-level-of-hilarious-incoherence-it-is-quite-amazing-to-see-the-contortions-the-ipcc-has/

[xlix] Patrick J. Michaels and Paul C. Knappenberger, *"Band-Aids can't fix the new IPCC report"*, September 27, 2013, https://www.cato.org/blog/band-aids-cant-fix-new-ipcc-report

[l] *"Media bias: Pretty much all of journalism now leans left study shows"*, November 11, 2018, https://www.investors.com/politics/editorials/media-bias-left-study/

[li] Ben Geman, *"Poll: Millennials care about climate change"*, February 26, 2018, https://www.axios.com/poll-millennials-care-about-climate-change-1519649123-0c3a4634-dd7b-4e12-a1a2-19fca93aa3b7.html

[lii] Cyrus Beschloss, *"Poll: climate change is top issue for youth voters in 2020"*, https://collegereaction.com/posts/poll-climate-change-is-top-issue-for-youth-voters-in-2020

[liii] UNESCO, *Climate change education,*
https://en.unesco.org/themes/education-sustainable-development/cce

[liv] Sarah Kaplan, Emily Guskin, *"Most American teens are frightened by climate change, poll finds, and about 1 in 4 are taking action",* September 16, 2019,
https://www.washingtonpost.com/science/most-american-teens-are-frightened-by-climate-change-poll-finds-and-about-1-in-4-are-taking-action/2019/09/15/1936da1c-d639-11e9-9610-fb56c5522e1c_story.html

[lv] Svante Thunberg Biography,
https://www.thefamouspeople.com/profiles/svante-thunberg-47914.php

[lvi] *"Pope tells Greta to carry on her fight",* April 17, 2019,
https://www.dw.com/en/pope-tells-greta-thunberg-to-carry-on-her-fight/a-48372358

[lvii] Matthew Taylor & Jonathan Watts, *"Climate crisis: 6 million people join latest wave of global protests",* September 27, 2019,
https://www.theguardian.com/environment/2019/sep/27/climate-crisis-6-million-people-join-latest-wave-of-worldwide-protests

[lviii] Bradford Richardson, " *Liberal professors outnumber conservatives nearly 12 to 1, study finds",* October 6, 2016,
https://www.washingtontimes.com/news/2016/oct/6/liberal-professors-outnumber-conservatives-12-1/

[lix] Lisa Wade PhD, *"Why are academics so liberal?",* January 20, 2010,
https://thesocietypages.org/socimages/2010/01/20/why-are-academics-so-liberal/

[lx] Jon A. Shields, *"The disappearing conservative professor",* Winter 2020,
https://nationalaffairs.com/publications/detail/the-disappearing-conservative-professor

[lxi] Common Dreams, *"7000 colleges and universities declare climate emergency, with a plan to fight it"*, July 11, 2019, https://www.ecowatch.com/climate-emergency-colleges-universities-2639161884.html

[lxii] David French, *"Here's how anti-conservative academic discrimination works"*, July 5, 2017, https://www.nationalreview.com/2017/07/conservatives-face-discrimination-colleges-keith-finks-ucla-case/

[lxiii] Paul Joseph Watson, "Google search blacklists major conservative websites in new censorship purge", July 21, 2020, https://summit.news/2020/07/21/google-search-blacklists-major-conservative-websites-in-new-censorship-purge/

[lxiv] Ellie Bufkin, "Twitter users appalled by bias and censorship plan boycott", June 24, 2020, https://townhall.com/tipsheet/elliebufkin/2020/06/24/conservatives-appalled-by-bias-and-censorship-plan-twitter-boycott-n2571231

[lxv] Coalition Publications News, "Global Warming: Facebook thinks its opinion is better than yours", June 12, 2020, http://co2coalition.org/2020/06/12/global-warming-facebook-thinks-its-opinion-is-better-than-yours/

[lxvi] *"Facebook must stop the spread of climate misinformation"*, July 1, 2020, https://www.climatepower2020.org/facebook-letter/

[lxvii] *"Climate movement drops mask, admits communist agenda"*, September 23, 2014, https://pjmedia.com/zombie/2014/09/23/climate-movement-drops-mask-admits-communist-agenda/

[lxviii] Jack Crowe, *"AOC's chief of staff admits the green new deal is not about climate change"*, July 12, 2019, https://www.nationalreview.com/news/aocs-chief-of-staff-admits-the-green-new-deal-is-not-about-climate-change/

[lxix] Alexander Kaufman, *"Bernie sanders unveils $16 trillion green new deal to combat climate change crises"*, https://www.huffpost.com/entry/bernie-sanders-climate_n_5d5e2104e4b0b59d256f42cc

[lxx] Ed Pilkington, *"Put oil firm chiefs on trial, says leading climate change scientist"*, June 22, 2008, https://www.theguardian.com/environment/2008/jun/23/fossilfuels.climatechange

[lxxi] Jessica Chasmar, *"Bernie Sanders to increase private jet use despite dire climate warnings"*, January 12, 2020, https://www.washingtontimes.com/news/2020/jan/10/bernie-sanders-to-increase-private-jet-use-despite/

[lxxii] Geoffrey Grider, *"20 Scientists ask Obama to put climate change deniers in jail"*, September 18, 2015, https://www.nowtheendbegins.com/20-scientists-ask-obama-to-put-climate-change-deniers-in-jail/

[lxxiii] Valerie Richardson, *"Bill Nye, the science guy is open to criminal charges and jail time for climate change dissenters"*, April 14, 2016, https://www.washingtontimes.com/news/2016/apr/14/bill-nye-open-criminal-charges-jail-time-climate-c/

[lxxiv] J. Kauppinen, P. Malmi, *"No experimental evidence for the significant anthropogenic climate change"*, June 29, 2019, https://arxiv.org/pdf/1907.00165.pdf

[lxxv] C.D. Idso, K.E. Idso, *"Carbon dioxide and Global warming, where we stand"*, http://www.co2science.org/about/position/globalwarming.php

[lxxvi] Investors Business daily editorial *"Another global warming study casts doubt on media's climate change fairy tale"*, November 30, 2017, https://www.investors.com/politics/editorials/another-global-warming-study-casts-doubt-on-medias-climate-change-fairy-tale/

[lxxvii] University Alabama *"Global Temperature Report Archives"* 1978 – 2019, https://www.nsstc.uah.edu/climate/archives.html

[lxxviii] *"University of Alabama finds global warming temperatures manipulated"*, July 25, 2019, https://metrovoicenews.com/university-of-alabama-finds-global-warming-temperatures-manipulated/

[lxxix] NOAA Research News *"Carbon dioxide levels hit record peak in May"*, June 4, 2019, https://research.noaa.gov/article/ArtMID/587/ArticleID/2461/Carbon-dioxide-levels-hit-record-peak-in-May

[lxxx] Medieval Warm Period (MWP1), https://www.thegrandsolarminimum.com/medieval-warm-period-mwp/

[lxxxi] Anthony Watts *"When the IPCC disappeared the Medieval Warm Period"*, March 10, 2010, https://wattsupwiththat.com/2010/03/10/when-the-ipcc-disappeared-the-medieval-warm-period/

[lxxxii] Sarah Gibbens, *"Your questions about our starving polar bear video answered"*, December 11, 2017, https://www.nationalgeographic.com/news/2017/12/starving-polar-bear-video-climate-change-spd/

[lxxxiii] *"Polar bear population decline a wake up call for climate change action. Southern Beaufort Sea polar bears show 40% drop in number"*, https://www.worldwildlife.org/stories/polar-bear-population-decline-a-wake-up-call-for-climate-change-action

[lxxxiv] Marc Morano, *"Study: Polar bear numbers reach new highs – population increases to highest levels in decades"*, March 5, 2019, https://www.climatedepot.com/2019/03/05/study-polar-bear-numbers-reach-new-highs-population-increases-to-the-highest-levels-in-decades/

[lxxxv] Laura Parker, Craig Welch, *"Coral Reefs could be gone in 30 years"*, June 23, 2017,

https://www.nationalgeographic.com/news/2017/06/coral-reef-bleaching-global-warming-unesco-sites/

[lxxxvi] Curtis Morgan, *"Coral in Florida Keys suffers lethal hit from cold"*, January 30, 2010, https://phys.org/news/2010-01-coral-florida-keys-lethal-cold.html

[lxxxvii] Peter J Mumby, *"Great Barrier Reef might not be dying after all"*, November 29, 2017, https://www.newsweek.com/great-barrier-reef-recovery-reefs-discovered-725517

[lxxxviii] Jennifer Marohasy, *"Coral catastrophes imagined"*, April 10, 2020, https://jennifermarohasy.com/2020/04/coral-catastrophes-imagined/

[lxxxix] Brian Kahn, *"Sea levels could rise by at least 20 feet"*, July 9, 2015, https://www.climatecentral.org/news/sea-levels-rise-20-feet-19211

[xc] Rose Moore, *"15 USA Cities that will be underwater by 2050 (10 already on the ocean floor)"*, November 17, 2019, https://www.thetravel.com/15-usa-cities-that-will-be-underwater-by-2050-10-already-on-the-ocean-floor/

[xci] *"14 U.S.Cites that could disappear over the next century, thanks to Global Warming"*, August 26, 2013, https://www.huffpost.com/entry/global-warming-flooding_n_3799019

[xcii] Chris Ciaccia, *"Sea levels to keep rising even if humanity hits climate targets, scientists warn"*, November 6, 2019, https://www.foxnews.com/science/sea-levels-to-keep-rising-even-if-humanity-hits-climate-targets-scientists-warn

[xciii] Alex Newman, *"UN IPCC Scientist blows whistle on lies about climate, sea level"*, February 12, 2019, https://www.thenewamerican.com/tech/environment/item/31472-un-ipcc-scientist-blows-whistle-on-un-climate-lies

[xciv] Alan Jones interviews Dr. Nils-Axel Mörner, August 19, 2019, https://youtu.be/e65JG4pj1tw

[xcv] Variation of 50-year mean sea level trends 9447130 Seattle, Washington, https://realclimatescience.com/wp-content/uploads/2015/12/2015-12-06-04-22-54.png

[xcvi] Sara Goudarzi, *"The real reason Louisiana is sinking"*, July 21, 2006, https://www.livescience.com/4186-real-reason-louisiana-sinking.html

[xcvii] United States Geographical Survey *"Land Subsidence"*, https://www.usgs.gov/special-topic/water-science-school/science/land-subsidence

[xcviii] Marc Morano, *"Analysis debunks absurd sea level rise claims about South Florida"*, May 16, 2017, https://www.climatedepot.com/2017/05/16/analysis-debunks-absurd-sea-level-rise-claims-about-south-florida/

[xcix] Jennifer Chu, *"Timeline of a mass extinction"*, November 18, 2011, https://news.mit.edu/2011/mass-extinction-1118

[c] Josh Davis, *"Over 270 new species described in 2018"*, December 27, 2018, https://www.nhm.ac.uk/discover/news/2018/december/over-270-new-species-discovered-in-2018.html

[ci] Eleanor Imster, *"Researchers describe 71 new species in 2019"*, December 11, 2019, https://earthsky.org/earth/new-species-discovered-in-2019

[cii] Salvatore Babones, *"Poor economy of scale: renewable energy is more about government policy"*, March 23, 2020, https://nationalinterest.org/blog/buzz/poor-economy-scale-renewable-energy-about-more-government-policy-133907

[ciii] Michael Hutchins, "Wind energy and birds FAQ – Part 1: Understanding the Threats", April 08, 2017, https://abcbirds.org/wind-energy-threatens-birds/

[civ] Marc Lallanilla, *"How do wind turbines kill birds?"*, May 14, 2013, https://www.livescience.com/31995-how-do-wind-turbines-kill-birds.html

[cv] Emma Bryce, *"Will wind turbines ever be safe for birds?"* March 16, 2016, https://www.audubon.org/news/will-wind-turbines-ever-be-safe-birds

[cvi] Michael Shellenberger, *"Democrats new climate plan will kill endangered species environmentalists fear"*, June 30, 2020, https://www.forbes.com/sites/michaelshellenberger/2020/06/30/democrats-climate-plan-will-kill-endangered-species-environmentalists-fear/#2d3354747571

[cvii] Nate Madden, *"When green energy isn't so green: retiring worn-out wind turbines is a wasteful process"*, September 11, 2019, https://www.theblaze.com/news/retiring-worn-out-wind-turbines-is-a-wasteful-process

[cviii] Chris Martin, *"Turbines tossed into dump stirs debate on wind's dirty downside"*, July 31, 2019, https://www.bloomberg.com/news/articles/2019-07-31/turbines-in-landfill-trigger-debate-over-wind-s-dirty-downside

[cix] Principia Scientific International, *"Millions of wind turbine blades to go to landfill"*, June 8, 2018, https://principia-scientific.org/millions-of-wind-turbine-blades-to-go-to-landfill/

[cx] Benjamin Zycher, *"The high cost of unreliable power"*, August 17, 2017, https://www.washingtontimes.com/news/2017/aug/7/energy-subsidies-for-solar-wind-put-oil-gas-at-dis/

[cxi] Eric Williams, Eric Hittinger, *"If we keep subsidizing wind, will the cost of wind energy go down?"*, August 6, 2017, https://www.pbs.org/newshour/science/keep-subsidizing-wind-will-cost-wind-energy-go

[cxii] *"The real life of solar panels"*, https://energyinformative.org/lifespan-solar-panels/

[cxiii] *"Can solar panels be recycled?"*, January 23, 2019, https://ecotality.com/can-solar-panels-be-recycled/

[cxiv] National Association of State Energy Officials *"The 2019 US Energy and Employment Report"*, https://www.usenergyjobs.org/2019-report

[cxv] *"Which states are most dependent upon on and gas activity?"* October 29, 2015, https://www.regiontrack.com/www/which-states-are-most-dependent-upon-oil-and-gas-activity/

[cxvi] Eben Harrell, *"Germany bans nuclear power"*, May 31, 2011, https://science.time.com/2011/05/31/germany-bans-nuclear-power/

[cxvii] Richard Martin, *"Germany runs up against the limits or renewables"*, May 24, 2016, https://www.technologyreview.com/s/601514/germany-runs-up-against-the-limits-of-renewables/

[cxviii] Soren Amelang, *"German households and industry pay the highest power prices in Europe"*, January 10, 2019, https://www.cleanenergywire.org/news/german-households-and-industry-pay-highest-power-prices-europe

[cxix] Amy Harder, *"Renewable energy mandates are costly climate policies"*, April 22, 2019, https://epic.uchicago.edu/news/renewable-energy-mandates-are-costly-climate-policies/

[cxx] Kevin Mooney, "How Virginia's Green New Deal will add to residents Covid-19 cost", June, 7, 2020, https://www.dailysignal.com/2020/06/07/how-virginias-green-new-deal-will-add-to-residents-covid-19-costs/

[cxxi] Barbara Maranzini, *"The hottest day on earth, 100 years ago"*, August 22, 2018, https://www.history.com/news/the-hottest-day-on-earth-100-years-ago

[cxxii] Linda Lam *"Hottest temperatures ever recorded in all 50 states"*, June 17, 2016, https://weather.com/news/climate/news/hottest-temperature-recorded-50-states

[cxxiii] Matthew Cappucci, *"Alaska's summer heat has been "basically of the charts"*, July 30, 2019, https://www.washingtonpost.com/weather/2019/07/30/alaskas-summer-heat-has-been-basically-off-charts/

[cxxiv] Tom V. Segalstad, *"The distribution of CO between atmosphere, hydrosphere, and lithosphere; minimal influence from anthropogenic CO on the global "Greenhouse Effect"*, https://folk.uio.no/tomvs/esef/ESEFVO1.pdf

[cxxv] Valerie Richardson, *"There is no climate emergency, hundreds of scientists, engineers tell UN"*, September 29, 2019, https://www.washingtontimes.com/news/2019/sep/29/scientists-tell-un-global-climate-summit-no-emerge/

[cxxvi] BBC News team, *"UK Parliament declares climate change emergency"*, May 1,2019, https://www.bbc.com/news/uk-politics-48126677

[cxxvii] Scottie Andrew and Saeed Ahmed, *"New York declares a climate emergency, the first US city with more than a million residents to do so"*, June 27, 2019, https://www.cnn.com/2019/06/27/us/new-york-city-declared-climate-emergency-trnd/index.html

[cxxviii] Fiona Harvey and Jillian Ambrose, *"Pope Francis declares "climate emergency" and urges action"*, June 14, 2019, https://www.theguardian.com/environment/2019/jun/14/pope-francis-declares-climate-emergency-and-urges-action

[cxxix] Bjorn Lomborg, *"The poor need cheap fossil fuels"*, December 3, 2013, https://www.nytimes.com/2013/12/04/opinion/the-poor-need-cheap-fossil-fuels.html

[cxxx] *EPA's report on environment (ROE)*, https://www.epa.gov/report-environment

[cxxxi] Van Cauwenberghe L, Janssen C, *"Microplastics in bivalves cultured for human consumption"*, 2014. Environmental Pollution, 193, 65-70,

http://www.ecotox.ugent.be/microplastics-bivalves-cultured-human-consumption

cxxxii *"Study finds microplastics in all remote Artic beluga whales tested"*, November 22, 2019, https://o.canada.com/pmn/news-pmn/canada-news-pmn/study-finds-microplastics-in-all-remote-arctic-beluga-whales-tested/wcm/71053f31-3aca-40f9-a2f3-90cc84f2b351

cxxxiii Chelsea Ritschel, *"Why is plastic bad for the environment and how much is in the oceans?"* April 18, 2018, https://www.independent.co.uk/life-style/plastic-bad-environment-why-ocean-pollution-how-much-single-use-facts-recycling-a8309311.html

cxxxiv Nick Routley, *"Visualizing the worlds top plastic emitting rivers"*, February 2, 2019, https://www.visualcapitalist.com/visualizing-the-worlds-top-plastic-emitting-rivers/

cxxxv Kelli Rogers, *"Asia-Pacific's plastic problem ignites waste management movement"*, January 10, 2019, https://www.devex.com/news/asia-pacific-s-plastic-problem-ignites-waste-management-movement-94115

cxxxvi Melissa Young, MD, *"Environmental toxins and your health"*, June 3, 2014, https://my.clevelandclinic.org/health/transcripts/1622_environmental-toxins-and-your-health

cxxxvii *"Countries that banned glyphosate weed killer"*, November 8, 2018, https://www.weedkillercrisis.com/topics/countries-that-ban-weedkiller-and-glyphosate/

cxxxviii *"List of 50+ foods containing weed killer ingredient glyphosate"*, March 31, 2019, https://www.weedkillercrisis.com/topics/list-of-foods-containing-glyphosate/

cxxxix Benedette Cuffari, *"Glyphosate in food: How dangerous is it?"*, https://www.news-medical.net/health/Glyphosate-in-Food-How-Dangerous-is-it.aspx

[cxl] Patricia Cohen, *"Roundup weed killer is blamed for cancers, but farmers say its not going away"*, September 20, 2019, https://www.nytimes.com/2019/09/20/business/bayer-roundup.html

[cxli] Steven R. Gundry, MD, 2019, *"The Longevity Paradox. How to die young at a ripe old age"*, New York

[cxlii] EPA, Colony collapse disorder, https://www.epa.gov/pollinator-protection/colony-collapse-disorder

[cxliii] Erick Motta, Kasie Raymann, Nancy Moran, *"Glyphosate perturbs the gut microbiota of honey bees"*, September 24, 2018, https://www.pnas.org/content/115/41/10305

[cxliv] Stephanie Strom, *"A Bee mogul confronts the crisis in his field"*, February 16, 2017, https://www.nytimes.com/2017/02/16/business/a-bee-mogul-confronts-the-crisis-in-his-field.html

Made in the USA
Columbia, SC
25 October 2020